The fine art of SPYING

KURT SINGER

W. SOMERSET MAUGHAM

ALAN HYND

WINSTON CHURCHILL

FRANZ VON RINTELEN

JOSEPH GOLLOMB

ANTHONY ABBOT

THOMAS M. JOHNSON

FLETCHER PRATT

The fine art of

SPYING

Edited by
WALTER B. GIBSON

Illustrated by
CAL SACKS

GROSSET & DUNLAP
Publishers   New York

ACKNOWLEDGMENTS

To the authors, their representatives, and the publishing houses who permitted the reprinting of copyrighted material, the following acknowledgments are gratefully offered:

Kurt Singer, PRISONER IN THE LEGATION. From "Spies Who Changed History." Copyright 1960 by Kurt Singer. Published by Ace Books, Inc., 1120 Avenue of the Americas, New York, New York.

THE TRAITOR. From "Ashenden" by W. Somerset Maugham. Copyright 1927, 1928, by W. Somerset Maugham. Reprinted by permission of the author, Doubleday & Company, Inc., and Messrs. William Heinemann Ltd.

Alan Hynd, ENCOUNTER AT TREASURE ISLAND. From "Betrayal from the East." Copyright 1943 by Robert M. McBride & Company.

I ESCAPE FROM THE BOERS. This abridgment of two chapters from "My Early Life: A Roving Commission," pp. 268-297, by Winston Churchill (copyright 1930 Charles Scribner's Sons; renewal copyright © 1958 Winston Churchill is used by permission of Charles Scribner's Sons. Acknowledgment is also made to Odhams Book Ltd., publishers of the British edition and proprietors of the copyright.

Peter Davies Ltd., THE DARK INVADER. From the book of that name by Franz von Rintelen.

Henry Gollomb, THE SPY WHO HAD TO DIE. From "Spies" by Joseph Gollomb. Copyright 1828 by The Macmillan Company.

Reprinted by permission of the author's estate. A VERY SPECIAL AGENT. From "These Are Strange Tales" by Anthony Abbot (Fulton Oursler.) Copyright 1948 by The John C. Winston Co.

Thomas M. Johnson, THE MASTER. From "Our Secret War." © Copyright 1929 by Thomas M. Johnson. © Copyright 1929 by NEA Magazine. © Copyright 1929 by The Crown Publishing Company.

Mrs. Inga Pratt Clark, THE CRYPTOGRAPHERS' WAR. From "Secret and Urgent" by Fletcher Pratt. Copyright 1939 by Fletcher Pratt.

Introduction

SPIES have been with us forever.

It's difficult to say why. The pay is poor, the work is hazardous, the consequences are commonly disastrous and final.

But still there are people who choose to make a career of duplicity and double-dealing. Despised by those who employ them, hunted by those who hate them, and haunted by the remnants of whatever conscience they once may have had, they live in a lonely world between worlds.

On the whole, spies are not lovable people—but they are often incredibly complex and interesting. They go about their surreptitious chores with the kind of industry and intelligence that would win fortunes for them in any honest endeavor.

Why? For love of country? For the exhilaration of the chase—as fox or hound? For the same suicidal reasons that prompt seemingly sane people to play Russian roulette? Because behind their masks they are able to find a satisfying sense of achievement by outwitting their unwitting dupes?

There is no single answer. The spy's motives are as obscure as his methods. You will be tempted, as you begin to explore the careers of some of the more notoriously devious operators, to try to find some character trait that would offer rational reason for their aberrant behavior.

Give up the search. I've been trying to find one for many years, and I am at last convinced that I have been searching for something that doesn't exist.

I've now settled down to the simple enjoyment of these dabblers in intrigue—and here, for your pleasure, are glimpses of some who have excelled at the fine and evil art of spying.

Like most interesting arts and endeavors, spying seems to be as old as the legends of mankind. A fine ancient example comes down to us in the story of a great wooden horse that stood outside the walled city of ancient Troy. Departing Greeks had left it after giving up a hopeless siege. Near it the Trojans found a wretched Greek traitor named Simon, who talked them into hauling the horse inside the city. That night, Simon rapped a signal and a picked crew of commandos dropped from the woodwork. The Greek force took over the city and the Trojan War was ended.

In the Bible we read how Moses sent twelve men to spy out the promised land of Canaan, which his followers later occupied with notable ferocity. But that was not until after his successor, Joshua, had sent two secret agents into the fortified town of Jericho to bring back data that aided the successful attack on that stronghold. Joshua, it is clear, had even more than the help of the Lord and trumpet players.

The Greek historian, Herodotus, relates how Periander, who inherited the throne of Corinth from his father, sent a messenger to Thrasybulus, tyrant of Miletus, asking for advice in ruling his subjects. Thrasybulus took the messenger for a walk in a cornfield, where he chatted about minor matters while breaking off all the finest ears that overtopped the rest and trampling them underfoot. He then sent the messenger back to Corinth.

There, Periander was eager to hear the answer to his query, only to learn that Thrasybulus had given none. All the messenger could talk about was the nonsensical way in which the Milesian tyrant had destroyed the cream of his corn crop while indulging in idle chatter. Periander, listening intently, recognized the point that the messenger had missed; namely, that his fellow-tyrant was advising him to crush any of his subjects who were ambitious to rise above the common herd.

Such empathy between members of the higher echelons, it seems to me, is the best form of secret communication ever devised.

Even in ancient days there were ways of sending messages through enemy territory unsuspected. Herodotus tells how a man named Demaratus informed the Spartans of an invasion planned by the Persian king, Xerxes. Messages were usually inscribed on wax spread over a wooden tablet, so Demaratus wrote his on the wood and covered it with wax. Since the bearer was carrying only a plain wax tablet, the Persians passed him through. Even in Sparta, they would have missed the idea, but for a woman named Gorgo, who suggested scraping off the wax to see what gave.

By the time of Lysander, a century later, more subtle trickery was the vogue. Whenever a messenger arrived, Lysander asked him for his leather belt. Lysander then wound the belt spiral fashion around a baton that he carried as his sign of rank. A message therewith appeared along the overlapping edges, for the sender had first wrapped the belt around an identical baton and had written the message in tiny letters which became nothing but decorative markings when the belt was straightened out.

Modern techniques have developed much more elaborate devices, ranging from plans of fortifications disguised as colored drawings representing butterflies to recordings made on rusty baling wire and documents reduced to microdots which are brought back to legibility under a powerful microscope.

Where there are spies, there are counterspies, and all of modern history is spotted with cases of ingenious duplicity. One of the neatest triple deals was staged by General James Oglethorpe, who founded the Colony of Georgia. Spaniards were advancing from Florida, so Oglethorpe hired a French spy to guide the English to the Spanish camp. There the traitorous Frenchman sprang ahead, fired a musket to rouse the Spaniards, and leaped safely in among them.

Oglethorpe's attack was foiled and he retired after a brief skirmish. Worse, he had to listen to his officers' complaints that he had been duped while the Frenchman had collected from both sides. The general smarted—and thought. Why not make it look as though the double-crosser was after a triple score? So Oglethorpe wrote a letter to the Frenchman, thanking him for what he had done, and telling him to keep the Spaniards thinking that the English forces were stronger than they were. He added that in a few days he would have reinforcements from Carolina and could stage a real attack instead of a sham.

Oglethorpe gave the letter (and a suitable sum of money) to a Spanish prisoner, telling him to go back to his camp and pretend he had escaped from the English, then slip the letter to the French spy. Of course the Spaniard turned over the money and the letter to his commander, who let loose his imprecations on the Frenchman, who was still denying the charges when they hanged him.

Then, sure that Oglethorpe's forces were weak—not strong, as the lying Frenchman had claimed—the Spaniards set out to attack the English camp, only to be ambushed by Oglethorpe. They still call the battlefield the "Bloody Marsh," which gives an idea of how thorough the massacre was.

Colonial espionage was generally poor stuff, and the spy work during the American Revolution was disappointing, too, compared with what went on abroad. There, the survival of such autocratic nations as France, Spain, and Austria depended on internal security rather than foreign intelligence, as the great danger lay within, not without.

But spydom thrived under Napoleon, whose first Lieutenant General, Fouché, created what amounted to the first police state. However, he unwisely chose to use his power to enter into an intrigue with England, so Napoleon ousted him in favor of a lesser light named Savary. The latter bought the services of a certain Karl Schulmeister, a smuggler from Alsace, who became a "double spy" in the Austrian service and adroitly brought their armies into a trap arranged by Napoleon.

A master of disguises, Schulmeister slipped free, and later returned to Vienna, where he continued to gull the Austrians. He was finally exposed and sentenced to be shot, but was saved by the timely arrival of the French army. But in the spy's world, skill is not always enough. Defeat drove the Austrians into an alliance with Napoleon, who married the Austrian princess, Marie Louise, and Schulmeister was forced into obscurity.

When the French Empire was restored under Louis Napoleon, armies of spies were needed to suppress opposing factions in France itself. That enabled Prussia to advance quietly but efficiently under a master spy named William Stieber, who introduced the forerunner of the modern "Fifth Column." While Louis Napoleon was worrying about his own safety in an opera bouffe atmosphere of plot and counterplot, Stieber assiduously employed his talents in buying malcontents. Due largely to his efforts, France was literally honeycombed with foreign espionage agents when the Franco-Prussian War struck in 1870.

The greatest and most cumbersome of all espionage organizations, the Russian Ochrana, the Czarist secret police, was the hunting ground for a remarkable opportunist named Ievno Aseff, whose career was perhaps the most fantastic of any on record.

While attending school in Germany, Aseff wrote to the Ochrana, offering to denounce Russian students with revolutionary leanings. He got the job. Soon, Aseff was working his devious way up as spy and counterspy, urging his comrades to outrages that resulted in the assassination of some of his own sponsors—Police Minister Pleheve and the Grand Duke Sergius, uncle of the Czar. By deftly playing

one side against the other and betraying both, Aseff industriously added to his own importance with each faction.
There is no evidence that he was at all disturbed that perhaps as many as a hundred people died in the promotion
of his career.

Aseff was a man of soaring ambition. He even arranged
for the assassination of the Czar himself. It was planned to
happen on a Russian cruiser during a review of the Baltic
fleet. But the appointed killers—two sailors with a revolutionary urge—balked at the last moment, when they learned
of an impending naval mutiny, which they decided should
come first. Such are the vicissitudes that beset the most
accomplished spies. The sailors in their slovenly way simply
decided to let the Czar's death wait, and before Aseff could
catch up with his own plot, the secret police finally caught
up with him.

But let no one think that industry goes unrewarded.
Aseff, killer of scores, managed to escape from Russia and
died quietly in bed in Paris years later. It's true. You can
look it up. There is a book about this monstrous man called
Aseff the Spy.

As I have said, it is difficult (and I now believe, impossible) to discover the sinister motives that drive these
lonely, amoral creatures to sell their own souls and the lives
of those around them for a few pieces of silver. With them
perversity passes understanding.

No matter. One can at least marvel at the complexities
of the human mind. And none, surely, is more curiously
complex than that of the spy.

Contents

Contents

Prisoner in the Legation

WHO knew what evil lurked within the gloom behind the deep-shuttered windows of the Chinese Legation in London?

There were rumors that a prisoner was held there by order of the Empress Dowager, head of the ruling Manchu dynasty. Would the freedom-loving British public storm those bastions and rescue the unknown captive?

Indeed, no. A foreign legation was inviolate according to civilized law in the year 1896, and the Chinese boasted the longest civilization in history. Besides, it was up to Downing Street to do something about it, and if the matter happened to be too secret or too confidential, Baker Street would handle it.

Of course, Winston Churchill hadn't yet come to Downing Street, and Sherlock Holmes never did live in Baker Street, but the "man in the street," as they called the average Londoner of that day, believed in both. So the average Londoner of that day did nothing but shake his fist outside the Chinese Legation, just as the average citizen of various countries today shakes his fist outside the American Legation.

But times were to change, and soon. Just two years later, Chinese insurrectionists in Peking murdered the German and Japanese ambassadors and drove others to the protection of the British Legation, where a force of five hundred

1

defenders maintained a state of siege. Relief finally came in the form of a six-nation expeditionary force, a forerunner of a modern United Nations mop-up detachment.

That made the Manchus both obsolete and insidious. So for years to come, fiction readers in England and America thrilled and chilled to the exploits of The Insidious Doctor Fu Manchu, until he, too, became as obsolete as his namesakes.

And so, today, who knows what evil lurks within the gloom behind the deep-shuttered windows of the Chinese Legation anywhere?

Nobody knows, but this is probable: if there should be a prisoner there, and he should happen to be a leftover from the insidious Manchu regime, he could expect a treatment that might shock even the experienced Empress Dowager were she still around.

Or, whoever he might be, and whatever might happen, the world outside would never know or even hear about it.

Times have changed since the Manchus held the prisoner in their London Legation. So let's get back to his story. It, at least, will remind us of the days when the world was civilized—or pretended to be—because it had nothing better to do.

Prisoner in the Legation

KURT SINGER

IT was a typical autumnal evening in London, rainy and foggy, that 1st of October 1896, when a young Chinese stepped out of the train at Euston Station. Only a few hours earlier he had disembarked from the *Majestic* when it docked at Liverpool. Throughout the ship's voyage from New York this passenger had kept more or less to himself.

In his early twenties, the young Chinese resembled the type of serious student from the Orient frequently seen in London. He wore a well-cut suit, had a neat little mustache and kept his black hair extremely close clipped. His walk was firm and springy, with a deliberately erect military carriage.

For such a young man the Chinese visitor had had an extremely adventurous career. In fact, he had circled the world, fleeing from his native country and the wrath of its

3

emperor. He had eaten the bitter bread of exile in Macao, Hong Kong, Singapore, Yokohama, Batavia, Honolulu, and San Francisco. And now he was in London, facing still more adventures. He hailed a hansom cab and asked the driver to take him to Haxell's Hotel in the Strand.

This new chapter in his life certainly seemed to be opening in a propitious manner. His hotel room proved very comfortable, the atmosphere of the hotel congenial. In spite of the fog and rain the young Oriental went out for a stroll in the city streets. The stream of carriages, the crowds, the mood of London, all struck him as pleasant. On the strength of these happy impressions he decided to look up a former teacher of his, Dr. James Cantlie, formerly head of the Medical College in Hong Kong and now back in London.

The Cantlies greeted their young visitor with warmth. Their home at 46 Devonshire Street, a typical London house with a small garden in the rear, struck him as charming. They had a great deal to talk about. The Cantlies were especially eager for the news of some of their mutual friends who seemed to have dropped out of existence in Imperial China. On hearing of something of the young man's recent experiences, and the circumstances which had brought him to London, Dr. Cantlie looked grave. "You know we don't live very far from the Chinese Legation," he said. "Don't you think you should pay your respects to the Chinese Government?"

Mrs. Cantlie, who did not always recognize her husband's jokes, demurred. "You'd better give that place a wide berth as long as you are here," she said. "They are quite capable of kidnapping you and shipping you back."

As a matter of fact, the Chinese visitor fitted into London almost as though it were his native city. His way of dressing was completely European, and his English was faultless. London gave him a feeling of exhilaration and it seemed that, for the time being, he had reached the end of his wanderings.

The following day he paid a call on another of his former teachers, Dr. Henry Manson. Here again he was warned to keep away from the Chinese Legation. The young man did not take these words too seriously. He might be wanted back in China, but here in London, half a world away, he was perfectly safe. He had by now moved from the hotel, and with the help of the Cantlies had found suitable lodgings in Gray's Inn Road. Eleven days after his arrival the young Chinese left his rooms and started out for Devonshire Street, where he was to visit the Cantlie family and accompany them to church. He had reached Oxford Circus, when a thought which had troubled him crystallized into certainty. He knew he was being followed and that, in fact, he was not far from the Chinese Legation at Portland Place, a thoroughfare which he had up to now studiously avoided. Glancing behind him, he saw a Chinese in mandarin attire standing only a few yards away. Nor was the man's proximity accidental, for now the Chinese quickened his steps and caught up with the student just as he crossed the road. With a polite smile the older man addressed the student:

"Are you a citizen of Japan or China, sir?" He spoke excellent English.

"Of China," said the student, glancing at his unknown interrogator.

"Of what part of China, may I ask?"

"Canton."

"That makes us compatriots. We speak the same dialect. I, too, am from Canton," said the unknown, slipping into Chinese.

The two strolled on together now, talking in their native language. They reached Cavendish Street and here suddenly another compatriot, also in mandarin clothing, made his appearance. Quietly, as though it were the most natural thing in the world, he joined the party, walking on the left side of the Chinese student.

The conversation rippled on, still in the politest Can-

tonese. The new member of the party invited his two
countrymen to his room for tea.

"I'm very sorry to have to refuse your invitation," the
student excused himself. "I am on the way to meet some
friends, and then we're going to church. Another time, perhaps."

Hereabouts and seemingly from nowhere a third Chinaman appeared, also in mandarin gown. The face of this man
was distinctly unattractive; he looked capable of any bru-
tality. Now the student's new friends dropped their pretense
of politeness. They seized their victim by his arms, steered
him around a corner, and there it was—49 Portland
Place. A door opened as though they were expected. The
student was hustled up the stairs and into the hallway.

He had not yet completely grasped the situation. It had
all happened so quickly, in broad daylight and in the
calm of a London Sunday. Could it be that the Chinese Secret Service had finally caught up with him, after he had
put half the world between them and himself?

A few minutes later he knew. He had been brought to a
huge room full of costly furniture, locked in and left alone.

There was an iron bar across the handsome door and he
was no longer in any doubt—he was being held captive in
the Imperial Chinese Legation. Back in Devonshire Street,
his friends the Cantlies would be waiting for him. Would
they realize what his absence meant, or would they think
he had simply forgotten his appointment? And what did the
people at the Legation have in mind for him? He took ref-
uge in a stoic calm which came easily to his Oriental tem-
perament. He would find that out soon enough.

Two hours later he was led to another room. He realized
he was on the second floor of the Legation building. Of this
latter fact there could be no doubt, since the only persons
in the corridors were Chinese, some in official dress. Two
Chinese, who maintained an obstinate silence, now came
and searched him. Most of his belongings were taken away,
even the watch in his pocket. He was now transferred to

yet another room, this time on the third floor. The small windows were heavily barred. The view was of rooftops, chimneypots, fog and smoke.

Sunk in thought, the prisoner was considering and marvelling at the speed and smoothness with which the kidnapping had taken place, when the door was unbolted. A tall, white-haired Englishman entered the "cell." Much later the student learned that he was Sir Halliday Macartney, a barrister who worked for the Chinese Government as counsellor and adviser.

"My dear young man," he began, "you are now on Chinese territory. To all intents and purposes you are in China, under Chinese law. May I have your name?"

The exile gave him it.

The Britisher smiled faintly. "We know better. Your name is Sun Wen." It was the name the student had used signing petitions for reform, political pamphlets and manifestos. "No sense beating about the bush, my dear young man," the Britisher continued. "We have been fully informed of all your movements. We had a message from the United States telling us that you were arriving on the *Majestic*. The Chinese Minister has requested your arrest."

"May I inquire why?"

"You know only too well. You have displeased your Emperor and your Government, haven't you?"

The prisoner remained silent. He had acted on deep convictions, knowing that to do that, under an absolutist Government, was a crime.

Meanwhile the Britisher continued his accusations. His heart was evidently in the case, and for a man so thoroughly western in appearance and demeanor he was certainly a loyal minion of his Chinese employer.

"Sun Wen, you drew up a petition calling for widespread reform and sent it to the Tsung-Li-Yamen in Peking, with the request that it be presented to the Emperor."

"I did."

"We in London have been ordered to detain you until

we find out the Emperor's personal wishes regarding you."

The prisoner could only too vividly imagine what form the Emperor's pleasure would take. He saw a headsman and a gleaming sword blade.

"May I inform my English friends of my presence at the Legation?"

"No, this you cannot do. You may, however, write a letter to your landlord instructing him to release your belongings, which will then be at your disposal."

The prisoner complied. That was all Sir Halliday cared to say to him for the present, for he strolled out of the room and left the young man to his thoughts.

In the notes he made on his imprisonment, he recorded this comment on the incident:

"It was very evident that my interrogator was playing a crafty game to get hold of my effects, and more especially my papers, in the hope of finding correspondence, whereby to ascertain who my Chinese accomplices were."

An hour later he was startled by a fearful noise. Carpenters were installing a second lock on his door. In addition to this, he gathered that two guards were being ordered to stand in front of his door to maintain an unceasing watch. Hearing the guards conversing in Cantonese, the prisoner tried to speak to them through the door, but they did not reply and instead entered the room and again searched him. This time they took away his keys and pocket knife. However, they failed to find a wad of banknotes he was carrying.

The day passed without further incident. In the late afternoon the guards asked him what he wanted to eat. Physically exhausted and psychologically drained, he asked only for a glass of milk. At seven, two English servants came to clean his room and bring coal and wood for the fireplace, but evidently they had strict orders and ignored his presence as though the room were empty.

He passed a restless night. Though the room was provided with a comfortable bed, he did not bother to undress. He could hear the guards talking, and from outside the windows the night noises of the city, the sound of trotting cab horses, the clatter of hoofs and rolling of wheels on cobblestones. Unwelcome thoughts crowded his mind. He was not afraid to die, but not this way—in an ignoble trap like this. Why did Macartney, an Englishman of high position, care to serve a feudal tyranny?

The next morning found the prisoner looking pale and peaked. His mind, however, was sharper than it had been the previous day, and he was determined to overlook no possibility for escape. He would try bribery. Above all, he must play for time. His friends had cautioned him not to go near the Legation. When they realized that he was missing, they would know where to look.

His first visitor that day was Kidnapper No. 1, the man who had engaged him in conversation on the street. He gave his name as Tang and identified himself as one of the many secretaries of the Imperial Chinese Legation.

The diary preserves this conversation. "Our first meeting," Tang said, "was more or less in line with official duty. I now come to talk to you as a friend. You had better confess that you are Sun Wen. There is no sense denying it. All arrangements have been made for your return to China."

Tang could not resist being sarcastic and said: "You are well known at home. The Emperor and the Tsung-Li-Yamen are acquainted with your activities. Just think what a wonderful chance you'll have to distinguish yourself, what a beautiful ending for a career, what an example you will be able to give of a courageous death. In that way you will become a real hero."

"Why do you assume I am going to die?" asked the prisoner, trying to sound out his captors' plans. "After all, I am not in China, but in England, a free country. What can you do to me here? Of course you could have me done away with right here in the Legation. That is certainly something you could easily do. But without a trial, such an act would be considered murder here, and these things have a way of leaking out. You wouldn't want any trouble with the Brit-

ish authorities. Then again, you might try to have me ex-
tradited, but such a procedure takes a long time. Besides,
the British Government would learn of my illegal imprisonment. I don't think the English would turn me over to
you anyway—this country has a tradition for providing
political asylum."

A sneer appeared on the face of the Legation secretary.

"Naturally we won't ask for extradition—that would be a
very stupid thing to do. A freighter is waiting for you in
Southampton right now. We will have no trouble at all in
pacifying you and transferring you from the Legation
building to the ship—after which you will of course be put
in chains. Before the ship reaches Hong Kong it will be met
by a gunboat which will take you aboard for Canton. That
is where your execution will take place."

"Without a trial, I suppose," the prisoner said dryly.

"The proper formalities will be observed. We are not
barbarians, you know. First the trial and then the behead-
ing," the middle-aged official answered politely and with
equal dryness.

"Don't you think you are running a risk? What if the
British police should get to know of this thing? I might
get word through or try to escape. Then you'd all be in hot
water."

Tang assured his prisoner that these eventualities were
extremely remote. He was well guarded here and there
would be no slip-up.

"Have you forgotten about the officers and crew of the
ship which is supposed to take me back?" asked the prisoner. "They will all know something is going on. The docks
are teeming with people. They're bound to notice something and make a stir."

Tang seemed unmoved. Everything had been thought of,
he said. The owners of the ship were close friends of Sir
Halliday Macartney. They were interested in trade with
China. He had their word for it that no untoward incident
would occur.

The more the prisoner talked with Tang, the more he would learn of the plot, he realized, and this could certainly be useful to him. Tang seemed not at all averse to discussing the arrangements, so perfectly sure was he that the situation was under control. For example, Tang told him that he would "travel" on one of the Glen Line steamers during the coming week. The Minister had not been willing to charter a ship exclusively for the purpose of conveying him to justice.

The prisoner pointed out that the enterprise looked rather difficult and complicated. One misstep and the whole thing would fall through. Hadn't they better change their minds and set him free?

Tang did not seem to appreciate this kind of humor. Not a muscle of his face moved as he replied: "You understand the problem very well. You are a clever man. Too bad you are not loyal to us and dream only of revolution. As it happens, you are right. We are not very pleased with this plan. If we had our way, we would dispose of you here in the Legation. That is a far more practical way of doing it. But our orders are to have you sent to China. The Emperor wishes it."

The prisoner's diary records more of this fateful conversation:

"For my edification and consolation, Tang then cited the case of a Korean patriot who, escaping from Korea to Japan, was induced by a countryman to go to Shanghai where he was put to death in the British concession. His dead body was sent back by the Chinese to Korea for 'punishment,' and on arrival there was decapitated, while the murderer was rewarded and given an important political post. Tang was evidently fondly cherishing the belief that he would be similarly promoted by his government for arresting me and securing my death. I asked him why he should be so cruel, to which he replied: 'This is by order of the Emperor, who wants you captured at any price, preferably alive.' "

The prisoner refused to lose his calm. As detachedly as if someone else's life were at stake, he continued to discuss various possibilities. "If the British Government should get to know of this it may declare all members of this Legation *persona non grata*. In which case you would have to return to China. My people in the province of Kwang-Tung would be on the lookout for a chance to revenge me. I hate to think what they would do to you and your entire family in payment for your act of treachery."

As the prisoner had guessed, this blow found its mark. Family feuds and bloody acts of revenge were very real concepts in the mind of Tang. He suddenly became apologetic and anxious to prove to the prisoner that he was only obeying orders. He was but a minor official—he had to do as his superiors commanded, no matter how personally repugnant it was to himself. . . . He asked for understanding and forgiveness. In fact, he became quite conciliatory and ventured to offer the young man a helpful suggestion.

"As I see it, you still have a small chance for life. What you must do is to deny that you had anything to do with the Canton plot and the reform plans. Accuse your accusers. Say that the whole thing is a trap sprung by the mandarins. Declare that you came voluntarily to the Legation to clear yourself and to ask for a review of your case."

It seemed a rather servile line to take. However, since no other course was open, the prisoner agreed to write such a letter. Perhaps it would soften the hearts of his kidnappers after all. Tang took the letter with a peculiar smile. It was the last the prisoner ever saw of him.

As the days went by, the young man had time to realize that he had fallen into a trap. He'd been foolish to write such a letter and acknowledge that he had come to the Legation of his own accord. This would clear the Legation with the British authorities, at least to some extent.

In despair as time ran out, he was ready to try anything, futile as it might seem, to reach the outside world. On two occasions he tried to smuggle notes to his friends, but none of the servants could be bribed. He wrote short notes on tiny bits of paper and threw them out of the window in the hope that some passer-by would find them. The first ones were caught in the wind, tossed up and whirled about for a moment. He watched them fall into a drain pipe on an adjacent roof.

He wrote other notes and weighted them with copper coins to make sure they would fall to the street. One fell into the garden of the adjoining house, No. 51 Portland Place, the home of Viscount Powerscourt. Another note fell on the roof of No. 53. The third and last fell on the street and was spotted by the Legation guards.

That was the end of the prisoner's attempt to draw attention to his plight. Some servants entered his room and fastened wooden boards over his windows. The room was now in total darkness.

"I was now worse off than ever," wrote the young man who had dared to defy an Emperor, "for my sole means of communication with the outside world seemed gone."

The prisoner had been raised as a Christian and he found consolation in prayer. He spent many hours praying, at least it seemed so, for he no longer had any way of estimating the passage of time. He didn't know whether one day went by or many. It was perpetual night in his room and blackest night in his soul. His only light came from the fire.

He had one last chance and that was to appeal to the two English servants who appeared daily to clean his room, bring him food and tend the fire. They performed their duties like machines, never speaking nor even seeming to see him. However, the younger of the two had a sympathetic face. His name was Edward Cole. So one morning the prisoner summoned up all his resolution and spoke to the man.

"Sir, will you not do something for me?" he asked.

To call a servant "sir" was sufficiently unusual for the man to start and look at the prisoner as though seeing him

for the first time. "Who are you?" he asked in low, frightened tones. "And what do you want of me?"

"I am a political refugee from China. I came to England
to seek the protection of the British Government. I am a
Christian just like yourself. You must have read in the
newspapers that the Sultan of Turkey is massacring the
Armenian Christians. Well, the Emperor of China wants to
kill me because I am a Christian, too. I belong to a political
party that wants good government and democratic freedom
for all in China, the way it is in England. I have done no
harm to anyone—I was brought here by trickery and am
being held under duress."

It was rash of him to say as much as he did, for the
guards might be listening outside the door. But he felt it
was the only way to win the man's sympathy.

Cole did not answer immediately. He busied himself
sweeping the floor and hearth. At last he said in a whisper:
"I don't know whether the British Government would want
to help you. After all, you are a foreigner and these people
are your own countrymen."

Desperation sharpened the prisoner's wits and urgently
he replied: "The British Government would surely help me.
That is why I am being kept here by force. Otherwise,
don't you see, the Chinese Government would have to ask
for my official extradition."

The impassive servant went on with his work. There was
no way of telling whether he felt sympathetic, or whether
the prisoner's plea fell on deaf ears. "My life is in your
hands, sir," the prisoner pleaded. "If the proper authorities
are informed of my confinement I shall be saved. Otherwise it means death for me. Is it not better to save a life than
to see it destroyed? Doesn't your duty as a Christian come
before your duty to your employers?"

One thing was certain—Cole had never been appealed
to in such terms before. He had always been a good, conscientious servant and discreet enough to realize that he
was not concerned in the business of his superiors.

With the calm impersonality of a perfect servant, he finished his work and withdrew.

It was another sleepless night for the prisoner. Had he won Cole over—or would Cole go to his employers and reveal all he had said?

In the morning Cole brought him his breakfast. He deposited it on a table and left, avoiding the prisoner's piteous eyes. Returning in the evening with a scuttle of coal, the servant again did not utter a word. Instead he pointed towards the scuttle he had brought in, and left the room.

Tucked in among the coals was a scrap of white paper. The prisoner snatched it up and read:

"I am willing to bring a letter to one of your friends, but not to the police. You must not write at the table as the guards can see through the keyhole. If you write on your bed, you cannot be seen from the hall."

The prisoner lay down on his bed and faced the wall. With a tiny stub of a pencil he wrote a message on an old and dirty visiting card of his. From this message, preserved for reasons which will be clear later in the story, we learn that the prisoner's written English was not as good as his speech.

His note read:

"To Dr. James Cantlie
46 Devonshire Street

"Please take care of the messenger for me at present, he is very poor and will lose his work by doing for me. I was kidnapped into the Chinese Legation on Sunday and shall be smuggled out from England to China for death. Pray rescue me quick? A ship is already chartered by C.L. for the service to take me to China and I shall be locked up all the way without communication to anybody. O! Woe to me!"

But the note was not delivered as its writer had written it. Cole waited until October 17th, a Saturday and his day off. Ever discreet, he did not deliver the prisoner's note, but sent one of his own by express messenger. It read:

"There is a friend of yours imprisoned in the Chinese Legation since last Sunday. They intend to send him out to China where it is certain that they will execute him. It is very sad for the poor man and unless something is done at once he will be taken away and no one will know it. I dare not sign my name but this is the truth, so believe what I say. Whatever you do must be done at once or it will be too late. His name is, I believe, Lin Yen Sen."

The Cantlies were enjoying a typical Saturday night at home, reading by the fireplace when this letter arrived. They had of course been aware of the defection of their Chinese friend, but they knew that Orientals often acted oddly by English standards and did not take his absence much to heart. They were sure he would turn up soon, with a perfectly good explanation for his behavior.

Cantlie knew that he had to act quickly. A professor of medicine, he knew little about investigations, spies, kidnapping and politics in general. But he knew that Sir Halliday Macartney was the legal counsel for the Chinese Government, so he decided to see him first. It never occurred to him to apply directly to the police. He happened to know that Sir Halliday lived nearby, at 3 Harley Place, in an impressive four-story building of gray stone. But the house was closed, the shades pulled down and the high iron gate locked. Perhaps its owner had gone to the country for the weekend.

A constable on duty in nearby Marylebone Road informed the anxious-looking gentleman that the house had been closed for at least six months. It was at this point that Dr. Cantlie decided to go to the nearest police station. There an inspector listened to his story and advised Cantlie to go to Scotland Yard.

The officers at police headquarters were extremely polite. But the story was so fantastic, so implausible and un-English, that they began to imagine that the doctor must be a crank or a bit potty. They listened and took down the facts. They would, they assured Dr. Cantlie, report the matter to their superiors. That was as far as Dr. Cantlie had got when, around midnight, he left and walked home.

There was not much he could do at that hour of the night, Cantlie decided. But he had no intention of leaving the matter there. At eight o'clock the next morning he was out of his house, consulting a friend. The two men deliberated a long time, and decided that if Scotland Yard failed to act it might be advisable to get someone to make a private approach to the Legation.

Once more Cantlie stopped at Harley Place, where he hoped to find at least the caretaker, who would tell him how to get in touch with Macartney. The place was completely deserted.

Finally Cantlie went home, exhausted from his long tramp across London. He found Cole waiting for him in the living room, and heard the "wild story" from the man's own lips.

Cantlie mentioned his fruitless visits to the Macartney residence. Cole raised his eyebrows. Sir Halliday was living in town and paid daily visits to the Legation, he said. In his opinion Macartney had a large part in the incident.

Cantlie immediately saw that this complicated the matter. A man of Macartney's standing had great power and influence. At this point Cole volunteered further information. Macartney, he alleged, had passed word around the Legation that the prisoner was a dangerous megalomaniac, who was being kept under lock and key for his own good. He was due to be shipped home on Tuesday. A captain and some sailors had come to the Legation to discuss the matter.

That gave them, Cantlie saw, forty-eight hours in which to act. He set off immediately to see his medical colleague, Dr. Manson. Together they went to Scotland Yard to make another appeal for help.

The officer on duty listened to their story. He consulted the records. "You were here on Saturday night," he said. "No new facts have turned up since to confirm your story."

In desperation the two doctors decided to go directly to the Foreign Office. It was not far, but gaining admittance was another story. They were politely informed that the clerk in charge could not see them before five in the afternoon.

They decided to wait and in due time were ushered into the office of this personage. He heard them out and with a shrug of his shoulders regretfully informed the gentlemen that since the day was Sunday, no action could be taken. He would report the matter to his superiors early next morning.

The doctors were dismayed. What if the Chinese should change their plans and ship the prisoner out a day earlier? They expressed their indignation: the entire British law enforcement system seemed to be in a state of paralysis because it happened to be Sunday.

The Foreign Office official tried to explain that this was a delicate matter involving foreign relations, diplomatic privileges, immunities and international law. He personally was not empowered to deal with such a problem. The doctors would have to wait as he had suggested.

The doctors, however, were not easily discouraged. They stood together outside the Foreign Office debating the next move and Cantlie suggested that although he was too well known to go to the Chinese Legation, there was no reason why Dr. Manson should not be admitted. He must go and take the bull by the horns. If he were not back within an hour, Cantlie would inform Scotland Yard.

It was already 6:30 P.M. when Dr. Manson rang the bell at No. 49 Portland Place. An exemplary English footman opened the door. Dr. Manson was led into an anteroom which was beautifully furnished with silver and gold brocades, bronze Buddhas and a huge portrait of the Emperor.

Dr. Manson had asked to see one of the attachés on an urgent matter. He had not long to wait before Tang entered the room. Bowing and smiling, the Chinese greeted the flustered Englishman who, waiving the usual formalities of greeting, stated the reason for his visit.

"A friend of mine, one of my former medical students in China, is being held prisoner in this Legation. I demand to see him."

Tang's face became cold, stony, and cruel.

"We have no prisoners in this Legation. What is the name of this young man you seek?"

"Sun Wen."

"No man of that name is under this roof."

"I know he is being held here, and so does Scotland Yard and the Foreign Office."

Tang remained imperturbable. He assured his excited visitor that it was all a great mistake. Perhaps someone was playing a joke on him. So convincing was the official's manner that Manson ended by believing him. When he rejoined Dr. Cantlie thirty minutes later, Manson told him that the story really was a bit preposterous. The people at the Legation knew nothing of the matter.

Dr. Cantlie, however, was more disturbed than ever. He could not subscribe to his friend's interpretation. In fact, he was convinced that the danger for his Chinese friend had increased as a result of the visit to the Legation. Something must be done quickly or the prisoner would be bustled on board the boat, which would perhaps leave earlier than planned. Then and there Cantlie decided to put a private detective on the job—to keep watch on the Legation in case an attempt was made to remove the prisoner. But then he remembered it was Sunday, a Victorian Sunday, and knew that nobody would be available.

Cantlie went back to Scotland Yard and implored them to set some detective to watch the Legation. He was told that the place was out of their zone; he was advised to go to the appropriate West End Police Station.

There the good doctor experienced his usual trouble in

making the officers see that this was a real emergency. In
the absence of concrete evidence the police had no authority
to place a guard over the Chinese Legation. As a last resort,
Cantlie offered a substantial sum to any constable off duty
who would undertake the surveillance as a private job. The
officers at the station were on duty all night; they were kind
enough to recommend a chap who lived in Islington, a retired member of the force, who was usually glad for a job
of some sort.

On his way to Islington Cantlie had to pass Fleet Street.
Here he had an inspiration. He walked into the offices of
The Times and asked to see a member of the editorial staff.

Nobody showed any eagerness to help him. The clerk in
the front office insisted that the gentleman state the reason
for the desired interview. Fuming with impatience, Cantlie
took the slip of paper the clerk offered and wrote these
words:

"Brutal kidnapping at the Chinese Legation; immediate
danger of death."

The receptionist looked quite dumbfounded. It was, apparently, not every day that visitors came with such messages. But the person in question would not be available
until ten in the evening. "Come back then," the clerk said.

"I will," Cantlie said grimly.

At Islington the doctor discovered that the retired member of the constabulary had something else he had to do that
night. He promised, however, to find a substitute.

By this time Dr. Cantlie was dead tired, having spent the
whole day on his quest for help. He was not a young man,
but he returned to *The Times* office, where a vigorous-look-
ing veteran journalist listened to this story. That it was an
astonishing story he was the first to admit. Still, it was of
such importance and delicacy, having regard to the circumstances, that he would be unable to do anything until it was
referred to the editorial board.

Dr. Cantlie left in utter disgust. He had knocked at every

possible door and been turned away. His efforts, it seemed, had failed completely.

It was eleven-thirty when he arrived home. Tired as he was, he was in no mood for sleep. His wife tried to calm him; together they discussed what else could be done. "Perhaps something will suggest itself in the morning," Mrs. Cantlie suggested. But this only made the doctor more restless. He couldn't go to sleep while that good young man might be being murdered. He was a medical scientist; his life had been devoted to teaching and research, and in the course of his work he had learned the value of persistence. One had to go on trying.

Operating on this assumption, Dr. Cantlie decided to skip sleep for one night. He put on some warmer clothes and set out for the Chinese Legation; he would watch it himself, he decided. He stayed there until the following morning and then paid a visit to Salter's Detective Agency as soon as it opened. There he engaged a number of agents to watch the Chinese Legation day and night.

His next call was to the Foreign Office, where he told his story once more, this time in the form of a sworn statement. The reaction here was not too encouraging. Officials pointed out that the only evidence was the alleged prisoner's own note claiming that he had been kidnapped. The rest was hearsay and could be very regrettable, diplomatically speaking, if it turned out to be a hoax.

The Foreign Office, however, asked Scotland Yard to investigate whether the Chinese Legation had made a charter or similar arrangement with any of the shipping lines.

Scotland Yard could work fast if it wanted to. The answer came promptly that such a charter had been drawn up with the Glen Line for a ship due to leave on Tuesday. The vessel had been chartered for a mixed cargo to China. There was also to be one passenger; his name was not given; he was merely identified as a Chinese national.

In the meantime the young man held behind the windows of the Chinese Legation was dying all the deaths which uncertainty can provoke. He had no idea whether Cole could be trusted sufficiently to have passed his message on to Dr. Cantlie.

The first real gleam of hope came when Cole brought in the usual evening scuttle of coal. Tucked into it was a note: "Be hopeful," it said, "we are working for you."

Still, this was no assurance that the rescuers would make it in time. Meanwhile Cole sent another note to Dr. Cantlie informing him:

> "I shall have a good opportunity to let your friend out on the roof of the next house in Portland Place tonight. If you think it advisable to have someone there waiting to receive him, and I am able to do it, find means to let me know."

Cantlie seized on this suggestion. He hurried to Scotland Yard again with a plea to have them put some police officers on the roof of the neighboring house. But the police decided against it. Such a procedure was beneath their dignity; the proper legal steps had been taken and soon the order would come through for the Legation to open its doors for inspection.

On October 22nd, England's great contribution to the rights of man, the writ of habeas corpus, was requested on behalf of the unknown prisoner, but unfortunately the judge before whom the application was made refused to grant it.

Nevertheless it brought England's newspapers into the fight. A reporter from the *Globe* called on Cantlie for a story and the doctor gave him the facts and also spoke of his visits to *The Times*.

That was the turning point. Other newspapers became interested in the prisoner in the Legation and soon reporters were swarming outside the house in Portland Place. They demanded to see the prisoner. Secretary Tang came out of his private office to talk to the reporters. Polite, smiling, utterly urbane, he assured the gentlemen that the story was a gigantic hoax put across by some joker with a wild imagination.

The reporters warned Tang that if the prisoner were not released within a day citizens might storm the Legation and free the hostage.

Tang went on smiling his subtle Chinese smile, seeming to imply that the journalists were surely joking, although he understood their flair for humor. It was apparent, though, that he failed to gauge the temper of the people of London, or the influence of the national Press.

Finally newspapermen tracked down Sir Halliday Macartney to Midland House. It was the *Daily Mail* which pulled off the scoop and printed the first interview with the legal representative of the Chinese Legation.

INTERVIEWS WITH SIR HALLIDAY MACARTNEY

Sir Halliday Macartney, Counsellor of the Chinese Legation, visited the Foreign Office at 3:30 yesterday afternoon. In conversation with a Press representative Sir Halliday said: "I am unable to give you any information beyond what has already appeared in print." On being informed that the Foreign Office had just issued an announcement to the effect that Lord Salisbury had requested the Chinese Minister to release the prisoner, Sir Halliday admitted that this was so, and in answer to a further question as to what would be the result of the request, replied, "The man will be released, but this will be done strictly without prejudice to the rights of the Legation involved."

In the course of a later conversation with a representative of the Press, Sir Halliday Macartney said: "Sun Wen is not the name of the man whom we have in detention upstairs. We have no doubt of his real identity and have been all the time fully informed of all his movements since he set foot in England. He came of his own free will to the Legation, and was certainly not kidnapped or forced or inveigled into the premises. It is quite a usual thing for a solitary Chinaman in

London to call here to make casual inquiries or to have a
chat with a countryman. There appears, moreover, to be
some ground for suspecting that this peculiar visitor, believing himself unknown, came with some idea of spying on us
and getting some information. Nobody knew him by sight.
When he called he got into conversation with one of our
staff and was afterwards introduced to me. We chatted for a
while and some remarks he made led me after he had gone
to suspect he might be the person we were having watched.
These suspicions being confirmed, he was on returning the
following day detained, and he is still under detention pend-
ing instructions from the Chinese Government."

Speaking of the international side of the matter, Sir Halliday said: "The man is not a British, but a Chinese subject.
We contend that for certain purposes the Legation is Chinese territory where the Chinese Minister alone has jurisdic-
tion. If a Chinaman comes here voluntarily and if there are
charges or suspicions against him, we contend that no one
outside has any right to interfere with his detention. It
would be quite different if he were outside this building, for
then he would be on British territory, and we could not arrest him without a warrant."

Answering further questions, Sir Halliday mentioned that
the man was not treated like a prisoner, and every consideration had been paid to his comfort. Sir Halliday ridiculed
the statement which had appeared that the captive might be
subjected to torture or undue pressure. He added a statement that a letter of inquiry had been received from the
Foreign Office on the subject, which would receive immediate attention.

The Central News says Sir Halliday Macartney, on his
return to the Chinese Legation from the Foreign Office,
proceeded to the bedside of the Minister Kung Ta Jen, and
explained to him that Lord Salisbury had insisted upon the
release of Sun Wen.

British newspapers came out with a rash of editorials,

waxing indignant at the uncivilized breach of international
law by the Imperial Chinese Government. Scotland Yard
posted guards outside the Legation. The harbor authorities, too, were alerted. By October 23rd the incident was
having repercussions at the highest level; Lord Salisbury,
Britain's Foreign Minister, issued a note of protest to the
Chinese Minister demanding the immediate release of the
prisoner. Two hours later, the Legation guards came to
"Sun Wen" and told him to put on his shoes, coat and hat
and to follow them downstairs. Was this the last act of his
kidnapping? Were the Chinese ready to ship him out? Or
was he going to be transferred to a cellar, where he could
more conveniently be shot?

"Where are we going?" he asked his impassive Chinese
guards, and received no answer.

The prisoner was led downstairs into a small reception
room. Three men were waiting for him, and lo and behold!
One of them was a friend. He had never welcomed the sight
of a man's face as he did the friendly visage of Dr. Cantlie.
Accompanying the doctor was Inspector Jarvis of Scotland
Yard, and a clerk from the Foreign Office. Neither Tang
nor Macartney were in the room, nor any member of the
Legation staff.

The doors were open; the four men walked out of the
Legation, where a huge crowd was massed to greet the
prisoner. Newspapermen from all parts were there to give
him a hero's welcome. The young man who had landed on
England's shore so unobtrusively three weeks ago was now
bombarded with hundreds of questions. The chief question
everyone asked him was: How had he managed to communicate with the doctor? But this was one question the ex-
prisoner would not answer. He had an obligation to the
quiet, colorless servant who had saved his life.

After a visit to Scotland Yard and a happy dinner at the
Cantlie home, the freed man wrote a letter of gratitude to
every London newspaper. No editor could know that this
letter was written by the man who was later to become the

first President of the Republic of China and founder of China's native democracy even though his friends had helped him to compose it.

The text of the letter has made history:

"Will you kindly express through your columns my keen appreciation of the action of the British Government in effecting my release from the Chinese Legation? I have also to thank the Press generally for their timely help and sympathy. If anything were needed to convince me of the generous public spirit which pervades Great Britain and the love of justice which distinguishes its people, the recent acts of the last few days have conclusively done so.

Knowing and feeling more keenly than ever what a constitutional government and enlightened people mean, I am prompted still more actively to pursue the cause of advancement, education, and civilization in my own well-beloved but oppressed country.

Yours faithfully
Sun Yat Sen." *

* Sun Yat Sen became China's great Socialist leader dedicated to overthrowing the Manchu régime and establishing a republic. He was the son of a poor Chinese farmer and as a student became associated with a secret revolutionary society. The failure of a plot led to the execution of several of the conspirators, but Sun Yat Sen escaped. At one time a reward of $300,000 for his capture was offered, but in 1912, on the onset of revolution, he became provisional President of the new republic. He died in 1925.

The Traitor

AROUND the year 400 B.C., a Chinese philosopher, Sun Tzu, wrote in his *Art of Warfare,* a special chapter on methods of espionage. Unquestionably, Sun Tzu's recommendations helped overthrow the feudal system then rampant in China. They did much more. They set a permanent pattern for the future, for the rules then laid down by Sun Tzu are even more pertinent today.

Picture a gigantic chessboard with thousands of squares, subdivided into varicolored sections. The board is studded with many forms of oddly shaped men, for although Sun Tzu used five basic types, composites are allowable, each with its own moves and limitations. These vary with the sections of the board, which represent home bases, enemy territory, and neutral terrain, with their colors subject to kaleidoscopic changes.

Some of Sun Tzu's men could hop into enemy lands and return. Others, if taken, belonged to the side that captured them. Still more could be lured to their destruction on squares of the wrong color, while others were deliberately sacrificed when their usefulness was ended.

An inhuman game, indeed, but that is the most human thing about it. For each of the pieces on such a board is endowed with its own failings and ambitions. They are self-actuating, never realizing that their moves are limited by

27

the master hand that has already taken their loves, their hopes, their desires, and their greed into complete calculation. For all are strands in a network designed by the artful Sun Tzu.

In their own little orbits, each plays the spider and tries to enmesh his opposite number, seldom realizing that he may be outwebbed and become a fly instead. But that still hinges on the hand that controls the master cord. For those who are most expendable seem to recognize it least. That, too, is the way of spydom.

In the tale that follows, we see such pawns in action. A great storyteller delves into their purposes, their daily lives, the fears that lurk beneath the blasé gloss that forms their stock-in-trade. The place was neutral Switzerland, the time, World War I. But it could have happened in World War II, instead; or, for that matter, in almost any war.

It might even be happening today, or tomorrow, anywhere, without any war at all, for without any question, much of this sort of thing did happen in the days of Sun Tzu, nearly twenty-five hundred years ago, and quite confidentially, such things have been happening ever since.

The Traitor

W. SOMERSET MAUGHAM

WHEN Ashenden, given charge of a number of spies working from Switzerland, was first sent there, R., wishing him to see the sort of reports that he would be required to obtain, handed him the communications, a sheaf of type-written documents, of a man known in the secret service as Gustav.

"He's the best fellow we've got," said R. "His information is always very full and circumstantial. I want you to give his reports your very best attention. Of course Gustav is a clever little chap, but there's no reason why we shouldn't get just as good reports from the other agents. It's merely a question of explaining exactly what we want."

Gustav, who lived at Basle, represented a Swiss firm with branches at Frankfort, Mannheim, and Cologne, and by virtue of his business was able to go in and out of Ger-

many without risk. He traveled up and down the Rhine,
and gathered material about the movement of troops, the
manufacture of munitions, the state of mind of the country
(a point on which R. laid stress) and other matters upon
which the Allies desired information. His frequent letters
to his wife hid an ingenious code and the moment she received them in Basle she sent them to Ashenden in Geneva,
who extracted from them the important facts and commu-
nicated these in the proper quarter. Every two months
Gustav came home and prepared one of the reports that
served as models to the other spies in this particular section
of the secret service.

His employers were pleased with Gustav and Gustav
had reason to be pleased with his employers. His services
were so useful that he was not only paid more highly than
the others but for particular scoops had received from time
to time a handsome bonus.

This went on for more than a year. Then something
aroused R.'s quick suspicions: he was a man of an amazing alertness, not so much of mind, as of instinct, and he
had suddenly a feeling that some hanky-panky was going
on. He said nothing definite to Ashenden (whatever R.
surmised he was disposed to keep to himself) but told
him to go to Basle, Gustav being then in Germany, and
have a talk with Gustav's wife. He left it to Ashenden to
decide the tenor of the conversation.

Having arrived at Basle, and leaving his bag at the station, for he did not yet know whether he would have to stay
or not, he took a tram to the corner of the street in which
Gustav lived, and with a quick look to see that he was not
followed, walked along to the house he sought. It was a
block of flats that gave you the impression of decent pov-
erty and Ashenden conjectured that they were inhabited
by clerks and small tradespeople. Just inside the door was
a cobbler's shop and Ashenden stopped.

"Does Herr Grabow live here?" he asked in his none too
fluent German.

"Yes, I saw him go up a few minutes ago. You'll find him in."

Ashenden was startled, for he had but the day before received through Gustav's wife a letter addressed from Mannheim in which Gustav by means of his code gave the numbers of certain regiments that had just crossed the Rhine. Ashenden thought it unwise to ask the cobbler the question that rose to his lips, so thanked him and went up to the third floor on which he knew already that Gustav lived. He rang the bell and heard it tinkle within. In a moment the door was opened by a dapper little man with a close-shaven round head and spectacles. He wore carpet slippers.

"Herr Grabow?" asked Ashenden.

"At your service," said Gustav.

"May I come in?"

Gustav was standing with his back to the light and Ashenden could not see the look on his face. He felt a momentary hesitation and gave the name under which he received Gustav's letters from Germany.

"Come in, come in. I am very glad to see you."

Gustav led the way into a stuffy little room, heavy with carved oak furniture, and on the large table covered with a tablecloth of green velveteen was a typewriter. Gustav was apparently engaged in composing one of his invaluable reports. A woman was sitting at the open window darning socks, but at a word from Gustav rose, gathered up her things, and left. Ashenden had disturbed a pretty picture of connubial bliss.

"Sit down, please. How very fortunate that I was in Basle! I have long wanted to make your acquaintance. I have only just this minute returned from Germany." He pointed to the sheets of paper by the typewriter. "I think you will be pleased with the news I bring. I have some very valuable information." He chuckled. "One is never sorry to earn a bonus."

He was very cordial, but to Ashenden his cordiality rang

false. Gustav kept his eyes, smiling behind the glasses, fixed watchfully on Ashenden and it was possible that they held a trace of nervousness.

"You must have traveled quickly to get here only a few hours after your letter, sent here and then sent on by your wife, reached me in Geneva."

"That is very probable. One of the things I had to tell you is that the Germans suspect that information is getting through by means of commercial letters and so they have decided to hold up all mail at the frontier for eight and forty hours."

"I see," said Ashenden amiably. "And was it on that account that you took the precaution of dating your letter forty-eight hours after you sent it?"

"Did I do that? That was very stupid of me. I must have mistaken the day of the month."

Ashenden looked at Gustav with a smile. That was very thin; Gustav, a businessman, knew too well how important in his particular job was the exactness of a date. The circuitous routes by which it was necessary to get information from Germany made it difficult to transmit news quickly and it was essential to know precisely on what days certain events had taken place.

"Let me look at your passport a minute," said Ashenden.

"What do you want with my passport?"

"I want to see when you went into Germany and when you came out."

"But you do not imagine that my comings and goings are marked on my passport? I have methods of crossing the frontier."

Ashenden knew a good deal of this matter. He knew that both the Germans and the Swiss guarded the frontier with severity.

"Oh? Why should you not cross in the ordinary way? You were engaged because your connection with a Swiss firm supplying necessary goods to Germany made it easy for you to travel backwards and forwards without suspicion. I can understand that you might get past the German sentries with the connivance of the Germans, but what about the Swiss?"

Gustav assumed a look of indignation.

"I do not understand you. Do you mean to suggest that I am in the service of the Germans? I give you my word of honor. . . . I will not allow my straightforwardness to be impugned."

"You would not be the only one to take money from both sides and provide information of value to neither."

"Do you pretend that my information is of no value? Why then have you given me more bonuses than any other agent has received? The Colonel has repeatedly expressed the highest satisfaction with my services."

It was Ashenden's turn now to be cordial.

"Come, come, my dear fellow, do not try to ride the high horse. You do not wish to show me your passport, and I will not insist. You are not under the impression that we leave the statements of our agents without corroboration or that we are so foolish as not to keep track of their movements? Even the best of jokes cannot bear an indefinite repetition. I am in peacetime a humorist by profession and I tell you that from bitter experience." Now Ashenden thought the moment had arrived to attempt his bluff; he knew something of the excellent but difficult game of poker. "We have information that you have not been to Germany now, nor since you were engaged by us, but have sat here quietly in Basle, and all your reports are merely due to your fertile imagination."

Gustav looked at Ashenden and saw a face expressive of nothing but tolerance and good humor. A smile slowly broke on his lips and he gave his shoulders a little shrug.

"Did you think I was such a fool as to risk my life for fifty pounds a month? I love my wife."

Ashenden laughed outright.

"I congratulate you. It is not everyone who can flatter himself that he has made a fool of our secret service for a year."

"I had the chance of earning money without any difficulty. My firm stopped sending me into Germany at the beginning of the war, but I learned what I could from the other travelers. I kept my ears open in restaurants and beer cellars, and I read the German papers. I got a lot of amusement out of sending you reports and letters."

"I don't wonder," said Ashenden.

"What are you going to do?"

"Nothing. What can we do? You are not under the impression that we shall continue to pay you a salary?"

"No, I cannot expect that."

"By the way, if it is not indiscreet, may I ask you if you have been playing the same game with the Germans?"

"Oh, no," Gustav cried vehemently. "How can you think it? My sympathies are absolutely pro-Ally. My heart is entirely with you."

"Well, why not?" asked Ashenden. "The Germans have all the money in the world and there is no reason why you should not get some of it. We could give you information from time to time that the Germans would be prepared to pay for."

Gustav drummed his fingers on the table. He took up a sheet of the now useless report.

"The Germans are dangerous people to meddle with."

"You are a very intelligent man. And after all, even if your salary is stopped, you can always earn a bonus by bringing us news that can be useful to us. But it will have to be substantiated; in future we pay only by results."

"I will think of it."

For a moment or two Ashenden left Gustav to his reflections. He lit a cigarette and watched the smoke he had inhaled fade into the air. He thought too.

"Is there anything particular you want to know?" asked Gustav suddenly.

Ashenden smiled.

"It would be worth a couple of thousand Swiss francs to you if you could tell me what the Germans are doing with a spy of theirs in Lucerne. He is an Englishman and his name is Grantley Caypor."

"I have heard the name," said Gustav. He paused a moment. "How long are you staying here?"

"As long as necessary. I will take a room at the hotel and let you know the number. If you have anything to say to me you can be sure of finding me in my room at nine every morning and at seven every night."

"I should not risk coming to the hotel. But I can write."

"Very well."

Ashenden rose to go and Gustav accompanied him to the door.

"We part without ill-feeling then?" he asked.

"Of course. Your reports will remain in our archives as models of what a report should be."

Ashenden spent two or three days visiting Basle. It did not much amuse him. He passed a good deal of time in the bookshops turning over the pages of books that would have been worth reading if life were a thousand years long. Once he saw Gustav in the street. On the fourth morning a letter was brought up with his coffee. The envelope was that of a commercial firm unknown to him and inside it was a typewritten sheet. There was no address and no signature. Ashenden wondered if Gustav was aware that a typewriter could betray its owner as certainly as handwriting. Having twice carefully read the letter, he held the paper up to the light to see the watermark (he had no reason for doing this except that the sleuths of detective novels always did it), then struck a match and watched it burn. He scrunched up the charred fragments in his hand.

He got up, for he had taken advantage of his situation to breakfast in bed, packed his bag, and took the next train to Berne. From there he was able to send a code telegram to R. His instructions were given to him verbally two days later, in the bedroom of his hotel at an hour when no one was likely to be seen walking along a corridor, and within twenty-four hours, though by a circuitous route, he arrived at Lucerne.

Having taken a room at the hotel at which he had been instructed to stay, Ashenden went out; it was a lovely day, early in August, and the sun shone in an unclouded sky. He had not been to Lucerne since he was a boy and but vaguely remembered a covered bridge, a great stone lion and a church in which he had sat, bored yet impressed, while they played an organ; and now wandering along a shady quay (and the lake looked just as tawdry and unreal as it looked on the picture-postcards) he tried not so much to find his way about a half-forgotten scene as to re-form in his mind some recollection of the shy and eager lad, so impatient for life (which he saw not in the present of his adolescence but only in the future of his manhood), who so long ago had wandered there. But it seemed to him that the most vivid of his memories was not of himself, but of the crowd; he seemed to remember sun and heat and people; the train was crowded and so was the hotel, the lake steamers were packed and on the quays and in the streets you threaded your way among the throng of holiday-makers. They were fat and old and ugly and odd, and they stank. Now, in wartime, Lucerne was as deserted as it must have been before the world at large discovered that Switzerland was the playground of Europe. Most of the hotels were closed, the streets were empty, the rowing boats for hire rocked idly at the water's edge and there was none to take them, and in the avenues by the lake the only persons to be seen were serious Swiss taking their neutrality, like a dachshund, for a walk with them. Ashenden felt exhilarated by the solitude, and sitting down on a bench that faced the water surrendered himself deliberately to the sensation. It was true that the lake was absurd, the water was too blue, the mountains too snowy, and its beauty, hitting you in the face, exasperated rather than thrilled; but all the same there was something pleasing in the prospect, an artless candor, like one of Mendelssohn's Songs Without Words, that made Ashenden smile with complacency. Lucerne reminded him of wax flowers under glass cases and cuckoo clocks and fancywork in Berlin wool. So long at all events as the fine weather lasted he was prepared to en-

joy himself. He did not see why he should not at least try to
combine pleasure to himself with profit to his country. He
was traveling with a brand-new passport in his pocket,
under a borrowed name, and this gave him an agreeable
sense of owning a new personality. He was often slightly
tired of himself, and it diverted him for a while to be merely
a creature of R.'s facile invention. The experience he had
just enjoyed appealed to his acute sense of the absurd. R.,
it is true, had not seen the fun of it; what humor R. possessed was of a sardonic turn and he had no facility for
taking in good part a joke at his own expense. To do that
you must be able to look at yourself from the outside and
be at the same time spectator and actor in the pleasant
comedy of life. R. was a soldier and regarded introspection
as unhealthy, un-English, and unpatriotic.

Ashenden got up and strolled slowly to his hotel. It was
a small German hotel, of the second class, spotlessly clean,
and his bedroom had a nice view; it was furnished with
brightly varnished pitch-pine, and though on a cold wet
day it would have been wretched, in that warm and sunny
weather it was gay and pleasing. There were tables in the
hall and he sat down at one of these and ordered a bottle
of beer. The landlady was curious to know why in that
dead season he had come to stay and he was glad to satisfy
her curiosity. He told her he had come to Lucerne to get
back his strength. He was employed in the Censorship
Department and was taking the opportunity to brush up
his rusty German. He asked her if she could recommend
to him a German teacher. The landlady was a blonde and
blowsy Swiss, good-humored and talkative, so that Ashenden felt pretty sure that she would repeat in the proper
quarter the information he gave her. It was his turn now
to ask a few questions. She was voluble on the subject of the
war on account of which the hotel, in that month so full
that rooms had to be found for visitors in neighboring
houses, was nearly empty. A few people came in from outside to eat their meals *en pension*, but she had only two

lots of resident guests. One was an old Irish couple who
lived in Vevey and passed their summers in Lucerne, and
the other was an Englishman and his wife. She was a German and they were obliged on that account to live in a neutral country. Ashenden took care to show little curiosity
about them—he recognized in the description Grantley
Caypor—but of her own accord she told him that they
spent most of the day walking about the mountains. Herr
Caypor was a botanist and much interested in the flora of
the country. His lady was a very nice woman and she felt
her position keenly. Ah, well, the war could not last for
ever. The landlady bustled away and Ashenden went upstairs.

Dinner was at seven, and, wishing to be in the dining
room before anyone else so that he could take stock of his
fellow-guests as they entered, he went down as soon as he
heard the bell. It was a very plain, stiff, white-washed room,
with chairs of the same shiny pitch-pine as in his bedroom,
and on the walls were oleographs of Swiss lakes. On each
little table was a bunch of flowers. It was all neat and clean
and presaged a bad dinner. Ashenden would have liked to
make up for it by ordering a bottle of the best Rhine wine
to be found in the hotel, but did not venture to draw attention to himself by extravagance (he saw on two or three
tables half-empty bottles of table hock, which made him
surmise that his fellow-guests drank thriftily), and so contented himself with ordering a pint of lager. Presently one
or two persons came in, single men with some occupation
in Lucerne and obviously Swiss, and sat down each at his
own little table and untied the napkins that at the end of
luncheon they had neatly tied up. They propped newspapers against their water jugs and read while they somewhat noisily ate their soup. Then entered a very old, tall,
bent man, with white hair and a drooping white mustache, accompanied by a little old white-haired lady in
black. These were certainly the Irish colonel and his wife
of whom the landlady had spoken. They took their seats and

the colonel poured out a thimbleful of wine for his wife
and a thimbleful for himself. They waited in silence for
their dinner to be served to them by the buxom, hearty maid.

At last the persons arrived for whom Ashenden had been
waiting. He was doing his best to read a German book and
it was only by an exercise of self-control that he allowed
himself only for one instant to raise his eyes as they came
in. His glance showed him a man of about forty-five with
short dark hair, somewhat grizzled, of middle height, but
corpulent, with a broad red clean-shaven face. He wore a
shirt open at the neck, with a wide collar, and a gray suit.
He walked ahead of his wife, and of her Ashenden only
caught the impression of a German woman self-effaced and
dusty. Grantley Caypor sat down and began in a loud voice
explaining to the waitress that they had taken an immense
walk. They had been up some mountain the name of which
meant nothing to Ashenden but which excited in the
maid expressions of astonishment and enthusiasm. Then
Caypor, still in fluent German but with a marked English
accent, said that they were so late they had not even gone
up to wash, but had just rinsed their hands outside. He had
a resonant voice and a jovial manner.

"Serve me quick, we're starving with hunger, and bring
beer, bring three bottles. *Lieber Gott,* what a thirst I have!"

He seemed to be a man of exuberant vitality. He
brought into that dull, overclean dining room the breath of
life and everyone in it appeared on a sudden more alert. He
began to talk to his wife, in English, and everything he said
could be heard by all; but presently she interrupted him
with a remark made in an undertone. Caypor stopped and
Ashenden felt that his eyes were turned in his direction.
Mrs. Caypor had noticed the arrival of a stranger and had
drawn her husband's attention to it. Ashenden turned the
page of the book he was pretending to read, but he felt
that Caypor's gaze was fixed intently upon him. When he
addressed his wife again it was in so low a tone that Ashenden could not even tell what language he used, but when

the maid brought them their soup Caypor, his voice still low, asked her a question. It was plain that he was inquiring who Ashenden was. Ashenden could catch none of the maid's reply but the one word *"lander."*

One or two people finished their dinner and went out picking their teeth. The old Irish colonel and his old wife rose from their table and he stood aside to let her pass. They had eaten their meal without exchanging a word. She walked slowly to the door; but the colonel stopped to say a word to a Swiss who might have been a local attorney, and when she reached it she stood there, bowed and with a sheeplike look, patiently waiting for her husband to come and open it for her. Ashenden realized that she had never opened a door for herself. She did not know how to. In a minute the colonel with his old, old gait came to the door and opened it; she passed out and he followed. The little incident offered a key to their whole lives, and from it Ashenden began to reconstruct their histories, circumstances, and characters; but he pulled himself up: he could not allow himself the luxury of creation. He finished his dinner.

When he went into the hall he saw tied to the leg of a table a bull terrier and in passing mechanically put down his hand to fondle the dog's drooping, soft ears. The landlady was standing at the foot of the stairs.

"Whose is this lovely beast?" asked Ashenden.

"He belongs to Herr Caypor. Fritzi, he is called. Herr Caypor says he has a longer pedigree than the King of England."

Fritzi rubbed himself against Ashenden's leg and with his nose sought the palm of his hand. Ashenden went upstairs to fetch his hat, and when he came down saw Caypor standing at the entrance of the hotel talking with the landlady. From the sudden silence and their constrained manner he guessed that Caypor had been making inquiries about him. When he passed between them, into the street, out of the corner of his eye he saw Caypor give him a sus-

picious stare. That frank, jovial red face bore then a look
of shifty cunning.

Ashenden strolled along till he found a tavern where he
could have his coffee in the pen and to compensate himself for the bottle of beer that his sense of duty had urged
him to drink at dinner, ordered the best brandy the house
provided. He was pleased at last to have come face to face
with the man of whom he had heard so much and in a day
or two hoped to become acquainted with him. It is never
very difficult to get to know anyone who has a dog. But he
was in no hurry; he would let things take their course: with
the object he had in view he could not afford to be hasty.

Ashenden reviewed the circumstances. Grantley Caypor
was an Englishman born, according to his passport, in
Birmingham and he was forty-two years of age. His wife,
to whom he had been married for eleven years, was of German birth and parentage. That was public knowledge. Information about his antecedents was contained in a private
document. He had started life, according to this, in a
lawyer's office in Birmingham and then had drifted into
journalism. He had been connected with an English paper
in Cairo and with another in Shanghai. There he got into
trouble for attempting to get money on false pretences and
was sentenced to a short term of imprisonment. All trace
of him was lost for two years after his release, when he re-
appeared in a shipping office in Marseilles. From there, still
in the shipping business, he went to Hamburg, where he
married, and to London. In London he set up for himself,
in the export business, but after some time failed and was
made a bankrupt. He returned to journalism. At the outbreak of war he was once more in the shipping business and
in August 1914 was living quietly with his German wife at
Southampton. In the beginning of the following year he
told his employers that owing to the nationality of his wife
his position was intolerable; they had no fault to find with
him and, recognizing that he was in an awkward fix granted
his request that he should be transferred to Genoa. Here

he remained till Italy entered the war, but then gave notice and with his papers in perfect order crossed the border and took up his residence in Switzerland.

All this indicated a man of doubtful honesty and unsettled disposition, with no background and of no financial standing; but the facts were of no importance to anyone till it was discovered that Caypor, certainly from the beginning of the war and perhaps sooner, was in the service of the German Intelligence Department. He had a salary of forty pounds a month. But though dangerous and wily, no steps would have been taken to deal with him if he had contented himself with transmitting such news as he was able to get in Switzerland. He could do no great harm there and it might even be possible to make use of him to convey information that it was desirable to let the enemy have. He had no notion that anything was known of him. His letters, and he received a good many, were closely censored; there were few codes that the people who dealt with such matters could not in the end decipher and it might be that sooner or later through him it would be possible to lay hands on the organization that still flourished in England. But then he did something that drew R.'s attention to him. Had he known it none could have blamed him for shaking in his shoes: R. was not a very nice man to get on the wrong side of. Caypor scraped acquaintance in Zurich with a young Spaniard, Gomez by name, who had lately entered the British secret service, by his nationality inspired him with confidence, and managed to worm out of him the fact that he was engaged in espionage. Probably the Spaniard, with a very human desire to seem important, had done no more than talk mysteriously; but on Caypor's information he was watched when he went to Germany and one day caught just as he was posting a letter in code that was eventually deciphered. He was tried, convicted, and shot. It was bad enough to lose a useful and disinterested agent, but it entailed besides the changing of a safe and simple code. R. was not pleased. But R. was not the man to let any desire

of revenge stand in the way of his main object and it occurred to him that if Caypor was merely betraying his
country for money it might be possible to get him to take
more money to betray his employers. The fact that he had
succeeded in delivering into their hands an agent of the
Allies must seem to them an earnest of his good faith.
He might be very useful. But R. had no notion what kind
of man Caypor was, he had lived his shabby, furtive life
obscurely, and the only photograph that existed of him was
one taken for a passport. Ashenden's instructions were to
get acquainted with Caypor and see whether there was any
chance that he would work honestly for the British: if he
thought there was, he was entitled to sound him and if his
suggestions were met with favor to make certain proposi-
tions. It was a task that needed tact and a knowledge of
men. If on the other hand Ashenden came to the conclusion
that Caypor could not be bought he was to watch and report his movements. The information he had obtained from
Gustav was vague, but important; there was only one
point in it that was interesting, and this was that the head
of the German Intelligence Department in Berne was growing restive at Caypor's lack of activity. Caypor was asking
for a higher salary and Major von P. had told him that he
must earn it. It might be that he was urging him to go to
England. If he could be induced to cross the frontier Ashenden's work was done.

"How the devil do you expect me to persuade him to
put his head in a noose?" asked Ashenden.

"It won't be a noose, it'll be a firing squad," said R.

"Caypor's clever."

"Well, be cleverer, damn your eyes."

Ashenden made up his mind that he would take no steps
to make Caypor's acquaintance, but allow the first advances to be made by him. If he was being pressed for results it must surely occur to him that it would be worth
while to get into conversation with an Englishman who was
employed in the Censorship Department. Ashenden was

prepared with a supply of information that it could not in the least benefit the Central Powers to possess. With a false name and a false passport he had little fear that Caypor would guess that he was a British agent.

Ashenden did not have to wait long. Next day he was sitting in the doorway of the hotel, drinking a cup of coffee and already half asleep after a substantial *mittagessen,* when the Caypors came out of the dining room. Mrs. Caypor went upstairs and Caypor released his dog. The dog bounded along and in a friendly fashion leaped up against Ashenden.

"Come here, Fritzi," cried Caypor, and then to Ashenden: "I'm so sorry. But he's quite gentle."

"Oh, that's all right. He won't hurt me."

Caypor stopped at the doorway.

"He's a bull terrier. You don't often see them on the Continent." He seemed while he spoke to be taking Ashenden's measure; he called to the maid, "A coffee, please, Fraülein. You've just arrived, haven't you?"

"Yes, I came yesterday."

"Really? I didn't see you in the dining room last night. Are you making a stay?"

"I don't know. I've been ill and I've come here to recuperate."

The maid came with the coffee and seeing Caypor talking to Ashenden put the tray on the table at which he was sitting. Caypor gave a laugh of faint embarrassment.

"I don't want to force myself upon you. I don't know why the maid put my coffee on your table."

"Please sit down," said Ashenden.

"It's very good of you. I've lived so long on the Continent that I'm always forgetting that my countrymen are apt to look upon it as confounded cheek if you talk to them. Are you English, by the way, or American?"

"English," said Ashenden.

Ashenden was by nature a very shy person, and he had in vain tried to cure himself of a failing that at his age was unseemly, but on occasion he knew how to make effective use of it. He explained now in a hesitating and awkward manner the facts that he had the day before told the landlady and that he was convinced she had already passed on to Caypor.

"You couldn't have come to a better place than Lucerne. It's an oasis of peace in this war-weary world. When you're here you might almost forget that there is such a thing as a war going on. That is why I've come here. I'm a journalist by profession."

"I couldn't help wondering if you wrote," said Ashenden, with an eager, timid smile.

It was clear that he had not learned that "oasis of peace in a war-weary world" at the shipping office.

"You see, I married a German lady," said Caypor gravely.

"Oh, really?"

"I don't think anyone could be more patriotic than I am. I'm English through and through and I don't mind telling you that in my opinion the British Empire is the greatest instrument for good that the world has ever seen, but having a German wife I naturally see a good deal of the reverse of the medal. You don't have to tell me that the Germans have faults, but frankly I'm not prepared to admit that they're devils incarnate. At the beginning of the war my poor wife had a very rough time in England and I for one couldn't have blamed her if she'd felt rather bitter about it. Everyone thought she was a spy. It'll make you laugh when you know her. She's the typical German *haus-frau* who cares for nothing but her house and her husband and our only child Fritzi." Caypor fondled his dog and gave a little laugh. "Yes, Fritzi, you are our child, aren't you? Naturally it made my position very awkward, I was connected with some very important papers, and my editors weren't quite comfortable about it. Well, to cut a long story short I thought the most dignified course was to resign and come to a neutral country till the storm blew over. My wife and I never discuss the war, though I'm bound to tell you that it's more on my account than hers, she's much more tolerant than I am and she's more willing to look upon this terrible business from my point of view than I am from hers."

"That is strange," said Ashenden. "As a rule women are so much more rabid than men."

"My wife is a very remarkable person. I should like to introduce you to her. By the way, I don't know if you know my name. *Grantley Caypor.*"

"My name is Somerville," said Ashenden.

He told him then of the work he had been doing in the Censorship Department, and he fancied that into Caypor's eyes came a certain intentness. Presently he told him that he was looking for someone to give him conversation lessons in German so that he might rub up his rusty knowledge of the language; and as he spoke a notion flashed across his mind: he gave Caypor a look and saw that the same notion had come to him. It had occurred to them at the same instant that it would be a very good plan for Ashenden's teacher to be Mrs. Caypor.

"I asked our landlady if she could find me someone and she said she thought she could. I must ask her again. It ought not to be very hard to find a man who is prepared to come and talk German to me for an hour a day."

"I wouldn't take anyone on the landlady's recommendation," said Caypor. "After all you want someone with a good north German accent and she only talks Swiss. I'll ask my wife if she knows anyone. My wife's a very highly educated woman and you could trust her recommendation."

"That's very kind of you."

Ashenden observed Grantley Caypor at his ease. He noticed how the small gray-green eyes, which last night he had not been able to see, contradicted the red good-humored frankness of the face. They were quick and shifty, but when the mind behind them was seized by an unexpected notion they were suddenly still. It gave one a peculiar feeling of the working of the brain. They were not eyes

that inspired confidence; Caypor did that with his jolly,
good-natured smile, the openness of his broad weather-
beaten face, his comfortable obesity and the cheeriness of
his loud, deep voice. He was doing his best now to be
agreeable. While Ashenden talked to him, a little shyly
still but gaining confidence from that breezy, cordial manner, capable of putting anyone at his ease, it intrigued him
to remember that the man was a common spy. It gave a
tang to his conversation to reflect that he had been ready to
sell his country for no more than forty pounds a month.
Ashenden had known Gomez, the young Spaniard whom
Caypor had betrayed. He was a high-spirited youth, with
a love of adventure, and he had undertaken his dangerous
mission not for the money he earned by it, but from a passion for romance. It amused him to outwit the clumsy German and it appealed to his sense of the absurd to play a
part in a shilling shocker. It was not very nice to think of
him now six feet underground in a prison yard. He was
young and he had a certain grace of gesture. Ashenden
wondered whether Caypor had felt a qualm when he delivered him up to destruction.

"I suppose you know a little German?" asked Caypor,
interested in the stranger.

"Oh, yes, I was a student in Germany, and I used to
talk it fluently, but that is long ago and I have forgotten.
I can still read it very comfortably."

"Oh, yes, I noticed you were reading a German book last
night."

Fool! It was only a little while since he had told Ashenden that he had not seen him at dinner. He wondered
whether Caypor had observed the slip. How difficult it was
never to make one! Ashenden must be on his guard; the
thing that made him most nervous was the thought that he
might not answer readily enough to his assumed name of
Somerville. Of course there was always the chance that
Caypor had made the slip on purpose to see by Ashenden's
face whether he noticed anything. Caypor got up.

"There is my wife. We go for a walk up one of the

mountains every afternoon. I can take you on some charming walks. The flowers even now are lovely."

"I'm afraid I must wait till I'm a bit stronger," said Ashenden, with a little sigh.

He had naturally a pale face and never looked as robust as he was. Mrs. Caypor came downstairs and her husband joined her. They walked down the road, Fritzi bounding round them, and Ashenden saw that Caypor immediately began to speak with volubility. He was evidently telling his wife the results of his interview with Ashenden. Ashenden looked at the sun shining so gaily on the lake; the shadow of a breeze fluttered the green leaves of the trees; everything invited to a stroll; he got up, went to his room and throwing himself on his bed had a very pleasant sleep.

He went into dinner that evening as the Caypors were finishing, for he had wandered melancholy about Lucerne in the hope of finding a cocktail that would enable him to face the potato salad that he foresaw, and on their way out of the dining room Caypor stopped and asked him if he would drink coffee with them. When Ashenden joined them in the hall Caypor got up and introduced him to his wife. She bowed stiffly and no answering smile came to her face to respond to Ashenden's civil greeting. It was not hard to see that her attitude was definitely hostile. It put Ashenden at his ease. She was a plainish woman, nearing forty, with a muddy skin and vague features; her drab hair was arranged in a plait round her head like that of Napoleon's Queen of Prussia; and she was squarely built, plump rather than fat, and solid. But she did not look stupid; she looked on the contrary a woman of character and Ashenden, who had lived enough in Germany to recognize the type, was ready to believe that though capable of doing the housework, cooking the dinner, and climbing a mountain, she might be also prodigiously well-informed. She wore a white blouse that showed a sunburned neck, a black skirt and heavy walking boots. Caypor, addressing her in English, told her in his jovial way, as though she did not know it already, what Ashenden had told him about himself. She listened grimly.

"I think you told me you understood German," said Caypor, his big red face wreathed in polite smiles but his little eyes darting about restlessly.

"Yes, I was for some time a student in Heidelberg."

"Really?" said Mrs. Caypor in English, an expression of faint interest for a moment chasing away the sullenness from her face. "I know Heidelberg very well. I was at school there for one year."

Her English was correct, but throaty, and the mouthing emphasis she gave her words was disagreeable. Ashenden was diffuse in praise of the old university town and the beauty of the neighborhood. She heard him, from the standpoint of her Teutonic superiority, with toleration rather than with enthusiasm.

"It is well known that the valley of the Neckar is one of the beauty places of the whole world," she said.

"I have not told you, my dear," said Caypor then, "that Mr. Somerville is looking for someone to give him conversation lessons while he is here. I told him that perhaps you could suggest a teacher."

"No, I know no one whom I could conscientiously recommend," she answered. "The Swiss accent is hateful beyond words. It could do Mr. Somerville only harm to converse with a Swiss."

"If I were in your place, Mr. Somerville, I would try and persuade my wife to give you lessons. She is, if I may say so, a very cultivated and highly educated woman."

"Ach, Grantley. I have not the time. I have my own work to do."

Ashenden saw that he was being given his opportunity. The trap was prepared and all he had to do was fall in. He turned to Mrs. Caypor with a manner that he tried to make shy, deprecating, and modest.

"Of course it would be too wonderful if you would give me lessons. I should look upon it as a real privilege. Naturally I wouldn't want to interfere with your work, I am just here to get well, with nothing in the world to do, and I would suit my time entirely to your convenience."

He felt a flash of satisfaction pass from one to the other and in Mrs. Caypor's blue eyes he fancied that he saw a dark glow.

"Of course it would be a purely business arrangement," said Caypor. "There's no reason that my good wife shouldn't earn a little pin-money. Would you think ten francs an hour too much?"

"No," said Ashenden, "I should think myself lucky to get a first-rate teacher for that."

"What do you say, my dear? Surely you can spare an hour, and you would be doing this gentleman a kindness. He would learn that all Germans are not the devilish fiends that they think them in England."

On Mrs. Caypor's brow was an uneasy frown and Ashenden could not but think with apprehension of that hour's conversation a day that he was going to exchange with her. Heaven only knew how he would have to rack his brain for subjects to discourse with that heavy and morose woman. Now she made a visible effort.

"I shall be very pleased to give Mr. Somerville conversation lessons."

"I congratulate you, Mr. Somerville," said Caypor noisily. "You're in for a treat. When will you start, tomorrow at eleven?"

"That would suit me very well if it suits Mrs. Caypor."

"Yes, that is as good an hour as another," she answered.

Ashenden left them to discuss the happy outcome of their diplomacy. But when, punctually at eleven next morning, he heard a knock at his door (for it had been arranged that Mrs. Caypor should give him his lesson in his room) it was not without trepidation that he opened it. It behooved him to be frank, a trifle indiscreet, but obviously wary of a German woman, sufficiently intelligent, and impulsive. Mrs. Caypor's face was dark and sulky. She plainly hated having anything to do with him. But they sat down and she began, somewhat peremptorily, to ask him questions about his knowledge of German literature. She corrected his mistakes with exactness and when he put before her some difficulty in German construction explained it with clearness and precision. It was obvious that though she hated giving him a lesson she meant to give it conscientiously. She seemed to have not only an aptitude for teaching, but a love of it, and as the hour went on she began to speak with greater earnestness. It was already only by an effort that she remembered that he was a brutal Englishman. Ashenden, noticing the unconscious struggle within her, found himself not a little entertained; and it was with truth that, when later in the day Caypor asked him how the lesson had gone, he answered that it was highly satisfactory; Mrs. Caypor was an excellent teacher and a most interesting person.

"I told you so. She's the most remarkable woman I know."

And Ashenden had a feeling that when in his hearty, laughing way Caypor said this he was for the first time entirely sincere.

In a day or two Ashenden guessed that Mrs. Caypor was giving him lessons only in order to enable Caypor to arrive at a closer intimacy with him, for she confined herself strictly to matters of literature, music, and painting; and when Ashenden, by way of experiment, brought the conversation round to the war, she cut him short.

"I think that is a topic that we had better avoid, Herr Somerville," she said.

She continued to give her lessons with the greatest thoroughness, and he had his money's worth, but every day she came with the same sullen face and it was only in the interest of teaching that she lost for a moment her instinctive dislike of him. Ashenden exercised in turn, but in vain, all his wiles. He was ingratiating, ingenious, humble, grateful, flattering, simple and timid. She remained coldly hostile. She was a fanatic. Her patriotism was aggressive, but disinterested, and obsessed with the notion of the superiority of all things German, she loathed England with a virulent hatred because in that country she saw the chief obstacle to their diffusion. Her ideal was a German world in which the rest of the nations under a hegemony greater than that of Rome should enjoy the benefits of German science and German art and German culture. There was in the conception a magnificent impudence that appealed to Ashenden's sense of humor. She was no fool. She had read much, in several languages, and she could talk of the books she had read with good sense. She had a knowledge of modern painting and modern music that not a little impressed Ashenden. It was amusing once to hear her before luncheon play one of those silvery little pieces of Debussy; she played it disdainfully because it was French and so light, but with an angry appreciation of its grace and gaiety. When Ashenden congratulated her she shrugged her shoulders.

"The decadent music of a decadent nation," she said. Then with powerful hands she struck the first resounding chords of a sonata by Beethoven; but she stopped. "I cannot play, I am out of practice, and you English, what do you know of music? You have not produced a composer since Purcell!"

"What do you think of that statement?" Ashenden, smiling, asked Caypor, who was standing near.

"I confess its truth. The little I know of music my wife taught me. I wish you could hear her play when she is in practice." He put his fat hand, with its square, stumpy fingers, on her shoulder. "She can wring your heartstrings with pure beauty."

"*Dummer kerl,*" she said, in a soft voice. "Stupid fellow," and Ashenden saw her mouth for a moment quiver, but she quickly recovered. "You English, you cannot paint, you cannot model, you cannot write music."

"Some of us can at times write pleasing verses," said Ashenden, with good humor, for it was not his business to be put out, and, he did not know why, two lines occurring to him he said them:

"Whistler, O splendid ship, the white sails crowding,
   Leaning across the bosom of the urgent West."

"Yes," said Mrs. Caypor, with a strange gesture, "you can write poetry, I wonder why."

And to Ashenden's surprise she went on, in her guttural English, to recite the next two lines of the poem he had quoted.

"Come, Grantley, *mittagessen* is ready, let us go into the dining room."

They left Ashenden reflective.

Ashenden admired goodness, but was not outraged by wickedness. People sometimes thought him heartless because he was more often interested in others than attached to them, and even in the few to whom he was attached his eyes saw with equal clearness the merits and the defects. When he liked people it was not because he was blind to their faults, he did not mind their faults but accepted them with a tolerant shrug of the shoulders, or because he ascribed to them excellencies that they did not possess; and since he judged his friends with candor they never disappointed him and so he seldom lost one. He asked from none more than he could give. He was able to pursue his study of the Caypors without prejudice and without passion. Mrs. Caypor seemed to him more of a piece and therefore the easier of the two to understand; she obviously detested him; though it was so necessary for her to be civil to him her antipathy was strong enough to wring from her now and then an expression of rudeness; and had she been safely able to do so she would have killed him without a qualm. But in the pressure of Caypor's chubby hand on his wife's shoulder and in the fugitive trembling of her lips Ashenden had divined that this unprepossessing woman and that mean fat man were joined together by a deep and sincere love. It was touching. Ashenden assembled the observation that he had been making for the past few days

and little things that he had noticed but to which he had
attached no significance returned to him. It seemed to him
that Mrs. Caypor loved her husband because she was of a
stronger character than he and because she felt his de-
pendence on her; she loved him for his admiration of her,
and you might guess that till she met him this dumpy,
plain woman with her dullness, good sense and want of
humor could not have much enjoyed the admiration of
men; she enjoyed his heartiness and his noisy jokes, and
his high spirits stirred her sluggish blood; he was a great
big bouncing boy and he would never be anything else and
she felt like a mother towards him; she had made him what
he was, and he was her man and she was his woman, and
she loved him, notwithstanding his weakness (for with her
clear head she must always have been conscious of that),
she loved him, *ach, was,* as Isolde loved Tristan. But
then there was the espionage. Even Ashenden with all his
tolerance for human frailty could not but feel that to betray your country for money is not a very pretty proceeding. Of course she knew of it, indeed it was probably
through her that Caypor had first been approached; he
would never have undertaken such work if she had not
urged him to it. She loved him and she was an honest and
an upright woman. By what devious means had she persuaded herself to force her husband to adopt so base and
dishonorable a calling? Ashenden lost himself in a laby-
rinth of conjecture as he tried to piece together the actions
of her mind.

Grantley Caypor was another story. There was little
to admire in him, but at that moment Ashenden was not
looking for an object of admiration; but there was much
that was singular and much that was unexpected in that
gross and vulgar fellow. Ashenden watched with enter-
tainment the suave manner in which the spy tried to in-
veigle him in his toils. It was a couple of days after his first
lesson that Caypor after dinner, his wife having gone upstairs, threw himself heavily into a chair by Ashenden's

side. His faithful Fritzi came up to him and put his long
muzzle with its black nose on his knee.

"He has no brain," said Caypor, "but a heart of gold.
Look at those little pink eyes. Did you ever see anything so
stupid? And what an ugly face, but what incredible charm!"

"Have you had him long?" asked Ashenden.

"I got him in 1914 just before the outbreak of war. By
the way, what do you think of the news today? Of course
my wife and I never discuss the war. You can't think what
a relief to me it is to find a fellow-countryman to whom I
can open my heart."

He handed Ashenden a cheap Swiss cigar and Ashenden,
making a rueful sacrifice to duty, accepted it.

"Of course they haven't got a chance, the Germans,"
said Caypor, "not a dog's chance. I knew they were beaten
the moment we came in."

His manner was earnest, sincere, and confidential. Ashenden made a commonplace rejoinder.

"It's the greatest grief of my life that owing to my wife's
nationality I was unable to do any war work. I tried to en-
list the day war broke out, but they wouldn't have me on
account of my age. But I don't mind telling you, if the war
goes on much longer, wife or no wife, I'm going to do
something. With my knowledge of languages I ought to
be of some service in the Censorship Department. That's
where you were, wasn't it?"

That was the mark at which he had been aiming and
in answer now to his well-directed questions Ashenden
gave him the information that he had already prepared.
Caypor drew his chair a little nearer and dropped his voice.

"I'm sure you wouldn't tell me anything that anyone
shouldn't know, but after all these Swiss are absolutely
pro-German and we don't want to give anyone the chance
of overhearing."

Then we went on another tack. He told Ashenden a number of things that were of a certain secrecy.

"I wouldn't tell this to anybody else, you know, but I

have one or two friends who are in pretty influential positions, and they know they can trust me."

Thus encouraged, Ashenden was a little more deliberately indiscreet and when they parted both had reason to be satisfied. Ashenden guessed that Caypor's typewriter would be kept busy next morning and that that extremely energetic major in Berne would shortly receive a most interesting report.

One evening, going upstairs after dinner, Ashenden passed an open bathroom. He caught sight of the Caypors.

"Come in," cried Caypor in his cordial way. "We're washing our Fritzi."

The bull terrier was constantly getting himself very dirty, and it was Caypor's pride to see him clean and white. Ashenden went in. Mrs. Caypor, with her sleeves turned up and a large white apron, was standing at one end of the bath, while Caypor, in a pair of trousers and a singlet, his fat, freckled arms bare, was soaping the wretched hound.

"We have to do it at night," he said, "because the Fitzgeralds use this bath and they'd have a fit if they knew we washed the dog in it. We wait till they go to bed. Come along, Fritzi, show the gentleman how beautifully you behave when you have your face scrubbed."

The poor brute, woebegone but faintly wagging his tail to show that however foul was this operation performed on him he bore no malice to the god who did it, was standing in the middle of the bath in six inches of water. He was soaped all over and Caypor, talking the while, shampooed him with his great fat hands.

"Oh, what a beautiful dog he's going to be when he's as white as the driven snow. His master will be as proud as Punch to walk out with him and all the little lady dogs will say: good gracious, who's that beautiful aristocratic-looking bull terrier walking as though he owned the whole of Switzerland? Now stand still while you have your ears washed. You couldn't bear to go out into the street with dirty ears, could you? Like a nasty little Swiss *schoolboy*.

Noblesse oblige. Now the black nose. Oh, and all the soap is going into his little pink eyes and they'll smart."

Mrs. Caypor listened to this nonsense with a good-humored sluggish smile on her broad, plain face, and presently gravely took a towel.

"Now he's going to have a ducking. Upsie-daisy."

Caypor seized the dog by the forelegs and ducked him once and ducked him twice. There was a struggle, a flurry and a splashing. Caypor lifted him out of the bath.

"Now go to mother and she'll dry you."

Mrs. Caypor sat down and taking the dog between her strong legs rubbed him till the sweat poured off her forehead. And Fritzi, a little shaken and breathless, but happy it was all over stood, with his sweet stupid face, white and shining.

"Blood will tell," cried Caypor exultantly. "He knows the names of no less than sixty-four of his ancestors, and they were all nobly born."

Ashenden was faintly troubled. He shivered a little as he walked upstairs.

Then, one Sunday, Caypor told him that he and his wife were going on an excursion and would eat their luncheon at some little mountain restaurant; and he suggested that Ashenden, each paying his share, should come with them. After three weeks at Lucerne Ashenden thought that his strength would permit him to venture the exertion. They started early. Mrs. Caypor businesslike in her walking boots and Tyrolese hat and alpenstock, and Caypor in stockings and plus-fours looking very British. The situation amused Ashenden and he was prepared to enjoy his day; but he meant to keep his eyes open; it was not inconceivable that the Caypors had discovered what he was and it would not do to go too near a precipice: Mrs. Caypor would not hesitate to give him a push and Caypor for all his jolliness was an ugly customer. But on the face of it there was nothing to mar Ashenden's pleasure in the golden morning. The air was fragrant. Caypor was full of conversation. He told funny stories. He was gay and jovial. The sweat rolled off his great

red face and he laughed at himself because he was so fat.
To Ashenden's astonishment he showed a peculiar knowledge of the mountain flowers. Once he went out of the way
to pick one he saw a little distance from the path and
brought it back to his wife. He looked at it tenderly.

"Isn't it lovely?" he cried, and his shifty green-gray eyes
for a moment were as candid as a child's. "It's like a poem
by Walter Savage Landor."

"Botany is my husband's favorite science," said Mrs. Caypor. "I laugh at him sometimes. He is devoted to flowers.
Often when we have hardly had enough money to pay the
butcher he has spent everything in his pocket to bring me a
bunch of roses."

"Qui fleurit sa maison fleurit son coeur," said Grantley
Caypor.

Ashenden had once or twice seen Caypor, coming in
from a walk, offer Mrs. Fitzerald a nosegay of mountain
flowers with an elephantine courtesy that was not entirely
displeasing; and what he had just learned added a certain
significance to the pretty little action. His passion for
flowers was genuine and when he gave them to the old
Irish lady, he gave her something he valued. It showed a
real kindness of heart. Ashenden had always thought botany
a tedious science, but Caypor, talking exuberantly as they
walked along, was able to impart to it life and interest. He
must have given it a good deal of study.

"I've never written a book," he said. "There are too many
already and any desire to write I have is satisfied by the
more immediately profitable and quite ephemeral com-
position of an article for a daily paper. But if I stay here
much longer I have half a mind to write a book about the
wild flowers of Switzerland. Oh, I wish you'd been here a
little earlier. They were marvellous. But one wants to be a
poet for that, and I'm only a poor newspaperman."

It was curious to observe how he was able to combine
real emotion with false fact.

When they reached the inn, with its view of the mountains and the lake, it was good to see the sensual pleasure

with which he poured down his throat a bottle of ice-cold
beer. You could not but feel sympathy for a man who took
so much delight in simple things. They lunched deliciously
off scrambled eggs and mountain trout. Even Mrs. Caypor
was moved to an unwonted gentleness by her surround-
ings; the inn was in an agreeably rural spot, it looked like a
picture of a Swiss châlet in a book of early nineteenth century travels; and she treated Ashenden with something less
than her usual hostility. When they arrived she had burst
into loud German exclamations on the beauty of the scene,
and now, softened perhaps by the food and drink, her eyes,
dwelling on the grandeur before her, filled with tears. She
stretched out her hand.

"It is dreadful and I am ashamed, notwithstanding this
horrible and unjust war I can feel in my heart at the moment nothing but happiness and gratitude."

Caypor took her hand and pressed it and, an unusual
thing with him, addressing her in German, called her little
pet names. It was absurd, but touching. Ashenden, leaving
them to their emotions, strolled through the garden and sat
down on a bench that had been prepared for the comfort of
the tourist. The view was of course spectacular, but it captured you; it was like a piece of music that was obvious and
meretricious, but for the moment shattered your self-control.

And as Ashenden lingered idly in that spot he pondered
over the mystery of Grantley Caypor's treachery. If he liked
strange people he had found in him one who was strange
beyond belief. It would be foolish to deny that he had
amiable traits. His joviality was not assumed, he was without pretence a hearty fellow, and he had real good nature.
He was always ready to do a kindness. Ashenden had often
watched him with the old Irish colonel and his wife who
were the only other residents of the hotel; he would listen
good-humoredly to the old man's tedious stories of the
Egyptian war, and he was charming with her. Now that
Ashenden had arrived at terms of some familiarity with
Caypor, he found that he regarded him less with repulsion

than with curiosity. He did not think that he had become a spy merely for the money; he was a man of modest tastes and what he had earned in a shipping office must have sufficed to so good a manager as Mrs. Caypor; and after war was declared there was no lack of remunerative work for men over the military age. It might be that he was one of those men who prefer devious ways to straight for some intricate pleasure they get in fooling their fellows; and that he had turned spy not from hatred of the country that had imprisoned him, not even from love of his wife, but from a desire to score off the bigwigs who never even knew of his existence. It might be that it was vanity that impelled him, a feeling that his talents had not received the recognition they merited, or just a puckish, impish desire to do mischief. He was a crook. It is true that only two cases of dishonesty had been brought home to him, but if he had been caught twice it might be surmised that he had often been dishonest without being caught. What did Mrs. Caypor think of this? They were so united that she must be aware of it. Did it make her ashamed, for her own uprightness surely none could doubt, or did she accept it as an inevitable kink in the man she loved? Did she do all she could to prevent it or did she close her eyes to something life would be if people were all black or all white and how much simpler it would be to act in regard to them! Was Caypor a good man who loved evil or a bad man who loved good? And how could such unreconcilable elements exist side by side and in harmony within the same heart? For one thing was clear, Caypor was disturbed by no gnawing of conscience; he did his mean and despicable work with gusto. He was a traitor who enjoyed his treachery. Though Ashenden had been studying human nature more or less consciously all his life, it seemed to him that he knew as little about it now in middle age as he had done when he was a child. Of course R. would have said to him: why the devil do you waste your time with such nonsense? The man's a dangerous spy and your business is to lay him by the heels.

That was true enough. Ashenden had decided that it

would be useless to attempt to make any arrangement with Caypor. Though doubtless he would have no feeling about betraying his employers he could certainly not be trusted. His wife's influence was too strong. Besides, notwithstanding what he had from time to time told Ashenden, he was in his heart convinced that the Central Powers must win the war, and he meant to be on the winning side. Well, then Caypor must be laid by the heels, but how he was to effect that Ashenden had no notion. Suddenly he heard a voice.

"There you are. We've been wondering where you had hidden yourself."

He looked round and saw the Caypors strolling towards him. They were walking hand in hand.

"So this is what has kept you so quiet," said Caypor as his eyes fell on the view. "What a spot!"

"*Ach Gott, wie schön!*" she cried. "*Wie schön!* When I look at that blue lake and those snowy mountains I feel inclined, like Goethe's Faust, to cry to the passing moment: tarry."

"This is better than being in England with the excursions and alarums of war, isn't it?" said Caypor.

"Much," said Ashenden.

"By the way, did you have any difficulty in getting out?"

"No, not the smallest."

"I'm told they make rather a nuisance of themselves at the frontier nowadays."

"I came through without the smallest difficulty. I don't fancy they bother much about the English. I thought the examination of passports was quite perfunctory."

A fleeting glance passed between Caypor and his wife. Ashenden wondered what it meant. It would be strange if Caypor's thoughts were occupied with the chances of a journey to England at the very moment when he was himself reflecting on its possibility. In a little while Mrs. Caypor suggested that they had better be starting back and they wandered together in the shade of trees down the mountain paths.

Ashenden was watchful. He could do nothing (and his

inactivity irked him) but wait with his eyes open to seize
the opportunity that might present itself. A couple of days
later an incident occurred that made him certain something
was in the wind. In the course of his morning lesson Mrs.
Caypor remarked:

"My husband has gone to Geneva today. He has some
business to do there."

"Oh," said Ashenden, "will he be gone long?"

"No, only two days."

It is not everyone who can tell a lie and Ashenden had the
feeling, he hardly knew why, that Mrs. Caypor was telling
one then. Her manner perhaps was not quite as indifferent
as you would have expected when she was mentioning a fact
that could be of no interest to Ashenden. It flashed across
his mind that Caypor had been summoned to Berne to see
the redoubtable head of the German secret service. When
he had the chance he said casually to the waitress:

"A little less work for you to do, Fraülein. I hear that
Herr Caypor has gone to Berne."

"Yes. But he'll be back tomorrow."

That proved nothing, but it was something to go upon.
Ashenden knew in Lucerne a Swiss who was willing on
emergency to do odd jobs and, looking him up, asked him
to take a letter to Berne. It might be possible to pick up
Caypor and trace his movements. Next day Caypor appeared
once more with his wife at the dinner table, but merely
nodded to Ashenden and afterwards both went straight upstairs. They looked troubled. Caypor, as a rule so animated,
walked with bowed shoulders and looked neither to right
nor to the left. Next morning Ashenden received a reply to
his letter: Caypor had seen Major von P. It was possible to
guess what the major had said to him. Ashenden well knew
how rough he could be: he was a hard man and brutal,
clever, and unscrupulous and he was not accustomed to
mince his words. They were tired of paying Caypor a
salary to sit still in Lucerne and do nothing; the time was
come for him to go to England. Guesswork? Of course it

was guesswork, but in that trade it mostly was: you had to deduce the animal from its jawbone. Ashenden knew from Gustav that the Germans wanted to send someone to England. He drew a long breath; if Caypor went he would have to get busy.

When Mrs. Caypor came in to give him his lesson she was dull and listless. She looked tired and her mouth was set obstinately. It occurred to Ashenden that the Caypors had spent most of the night talking. He wished he knew what they had said. Did she urge him to go or did she try to dissuade him? Ashenden watched them again at luncheon. Something was the matter, for they hardly spoke to one another and as a rule they found plenty to talk about. They left the room early, but when Ashenden went out he saw Caypor sitting in the hall by himself.

"Hulloa," he cried jovially, but surely the effort was patent, "how are you getting on? I've been to Geneva."

"So I heard," said Ashenden.

"Come and have your coffee with me. My poor wife's got a headache. I told her she'd better go and lie down." In his shifty green eyes was an expression that Ashenden could not read. "The fact is, she's rather worried, poor dear; I'm thinking of going to England."

Ashenden's heart gave a sudden leap against his ribs, but his face remained impassive.

"Oh, are you going for long? We shall miss you."

"To tell the truth, I'm fed up with doing nothing. The war looks as though it were going on for years and I can't sit here indefinitely. Besides, I can't afford it, I've got to earn my living. I may have a German wife, but I am an Englishman, hang it all, and I want to do my bit. I could never face my friends again if I just stayed here in ease and comfort till the end of the war and never attempted to do a thing to help the country. My wife takes her German point of view and I don't mind telling you she's a bit upset. You know what women are."

Now Ashenden knew what it was that he saw in Caypor's

eyes. Fear. It gave him a nasty turn. Caypor didn't want to go to England, he wanted to stay safely in Switzerland; Ashenden knew now what the major had said to him when he went to see him in Berne. He had got to go or lose his salary. What was it that his wife had said when he told her what had happened? He had wanted her to press him to stay, but it was plain, she hadn't done that; perhaps he had not dared tell her how frightened he was; to her he had always been gay, bold, adventurous, and devil-may-care, and now, the prisoner of his own lies, he had not found it in him to confess himself the mean and sneaking coward he was.

"Are you going to take your wife with you?" asked Ashenden.

"No, she'll stay here."

It had been arranged very neatly. Mrs. Caypor would receive his letters and forward the information they contained to Berne.

"I've been out of England so long that I don't quite know how to set about getting war work. What would you do in my place?"

"I don't know; what sort of work are you thinking of?"

"Well, you know, I imagine I could do the same thing as you did. I wonder if there's anyone in the Censorship Department that you could give me a letter of introduction to."

It was only by a miracle that Ashenden saved himself from showing by a smothered cry or by a broken gesture how startled he was; but not by Caypor's request, by what had just dawned on him. What an idiot he had been! He had been disturbed by the thought that he was wasting his time at Lucerne, he was doing nothing, and though in fact, as it turned out, Caypor was going to England it was due to no cleverness of his. He could take to himself no credit for the result. And now he saw that he had been put in Lucerne, told how to describe himself and given the proper information, so that what actually had occurred should occur. It would be a wonderful thing for the German secret

service to get an agent into the Censorship Department;
and by a happy accident there was Grantley Caypor, the
very man for the job, on friendly terms with someone who
had worked there. What a bit of luck! Major von P. was a
man of culture and, rubbing his hands, he must surely have
murmured: *stultum facit fortuna quem vult perdere*. It was
a trap of that devilish R. and the grim major at Berne had
fallen into it. Ashenden had done his work just by sitting
still and doing nothing. He almost laughed as he thought
what a fool R. had made of him.

"I was on very good terms with the chief of my department, I could give you a note to him if you liked."

"That would be just the thing."

"But of course I must give the facts. I must say I've met
you here and only known you a fortnight."

"Of course. But you'll say what else you can for me,
won't you?"

"Oh, certainly."

"I don't know yet if I can get a visa. I'm told they're
rather fussy."

"I don't see why. I shall be very sick if they refuse me
one when I want to go back."

"I'll go and see how my wife is getting on," said Caypor suddenly, getting up. "When will you let me have that
letter?"

"Whenever you like. Are you going at once?"

"As soon as possible."

Caypor left him. Ashenden waited in the hall for a quarter of an hour so that there should appear in him no sign of
hurry. Then he went upstairs and prepared various communications. In one he informed R. that Caypor was going
to England; in another he made arrangements through
Berne that wherever Caypor applied for a visa it should be
granted to him without question; and these he dispatched
forthwith. When he went down to dinner he handed Caypor
a cordial letter of introduction.

Next day but one Caypor left Lucerne.

Ashenden waited. He continued to have his hour's lesson

with Mrs. Caypor and under her conscientious tuition began now to speak German with ease. They talked of Goethe and Winckelmann, of art and life and travel. Fritzi sat quietly by her chair.

"He misses his master," she said, pulling his ears. "He only really cares for him, he suffers me only as belonging to him."

After his lesson Ashenden went every morning to Cook's to ask for his letters. It was here that all communications were addressed to him. He could not move till he received instructions, but R. could be trusted not to leave him idle for long; and meanwhile there was nothing for him to do but have patience. Presently he received a letter from the Consul in Geneva to say that Caypor had there applied for his visa and had set out for France. Having read this, Ashenden went on for a little stroll by the lake and on his way back happened to see Mrs. Caypor coming out of Cook's office. He guessed that she was having her letters addressed there too. He went up to her.

"Have you had news of Herr Caypor?" he asked her.

"No," she said. "I suppose I could hardly expect to yet."

He walked along by her side. She was disappointed, but not yet anxious; she knew how irregular at that time was the post. But next day during the lesson he could not but see that she was impatient to have done with it. The post was delivered at noon and at five minutes to she looked at her watch and him. Though Ashenden knew very well that no letter would ever come for her he had not the heart to keep her on tenterhooks.

"Don't you think that's enough for the day? I'm sure you want to go down to Cook's," he said.

"Thank you. That is very amiable of you."

Later he went there himself and he found her standing in the middle of the office. Her face was distraught. She addressed him wildly.

"My husband promised to write from Paris. I am sure there is a letter for me, but these stupid people say there's nothing. They're so careless, it's a scandal."

Ashenden did not know what to say. While the clerk was looking through the bundle to see if there was anything for him she came up to the desk again.

"When does the next post come in from France?" she asked.

"Sometimes there are letters about five."

"I'll come then."

She turned and walked rapidly away. Fritzi followed her with his tail between his legs. There was no doubt of it, already the fear had seized her that something was wrong. Next morning she looked dreadful; she could not have closed her eyes all night; and in the middle of the lesson she started up from her chair.

"You must excuse me, Herr Somerville, I cannot give you a lesson today, I am not feeling well."

Before Ashenden could say anything she had flung nervously from the room, and in the evening he got a note from her to say that she regretted that she must discontinue giving him conversation lessons. She gave no reason. Then Ashenden saw no more of her; she ceased coming in to meals; except to go morning and afternoon to Cook's she spent apparently the whole day in her room. Ashenden thought of her sitting there hour after hour with that hideous fear gnawing at her heart. Who could help feeling sorry for her? The time hung heavy on his hands too. He read a good deal and wrote a little, he hired a canoe and went for long leisurely paddles on the lake; and at last one morning the clerk at Cook's handed him a letter. It was from R. It had all the appearance of a business communication, but between the lines he read a good deal.

Dear Sir, it began, The goods, with accompanying letter, dispatched by you from Lucerne have been duly delivered. We are obliged to you for executing our instructions with such promptness.

It went on in this strain. R. was exultant. Ashenden guessed that Caypor had been arrested and by now had paid the penalty of his crime. He shuddered. He remembered a dreadful scene. Dawn. A cold gray dawn, with a

drizzling rain falling. A man, blindfolded, standing against
a wall, an officer very pale giving an order, a volley, and
then a young soldier, one of the firing party, turning round
and holding on to his gun for support, vomiting. The
officer turned paler still, and he, Ashenden, feeling dread-
fully faint. How terrified Caypor must have been! It was
awful when the tears ran down their faces. Ashenden shook
himself. He went to the ticket office and obedient to his
orders bought himself a ticket for Geneva.

As he was waiting for his change Mrs. Caypor came in.
He was shocked at the sight of her. She was blowsy and di-
shevelled and there were heavy rings round her eyes. She
was deathly pale. She staggered up to the desk and asked
for a letter. The clerk shook his head.

"I'm sorry, madam, there's nothing yet."

"But look, look. Are you sure? Please look again."

The misery in her voice was heartrending. The clerk
with a shrug of the shoulders took out the letters from a
pigeonhole and sorted them once more.

"No, there's nothing, madam."

She gave a hoarse cry of despair and her face was dis-
torted with anguish.

"Oh God, oh God," she moaned.

She turned away, the tears streaming from her eyes, and
for a moment she stood there like a blind man groping and
not knowing which way to go. Then a fearful thing happened. Fritzi, the bull terrier, sat down on his haunches
and threw back his head and gave a long, long melancholy
howl. Mrs. Caypor looked at him with terror; her eyes
seemed really to start from her head. The doubt, the gnawing doubt that had tortured her during those dreadful days
of suspense, was a doubt no longer. She knew. She staggered blindly into the street.

Encounter at Treasure Island

AH, for the dear, dead days of the silent cinema, when people sat fascinated amid the flickery twilight of a double comedy festival! It cost all of fifteen cents, a dime for admission and a nickel for a king-sized bag of buttered popcorn that you munched as an obligato to the tinny tunes of a beaten-up piano. Whenever titles were flashed on the screen, everybody read them aloud, so that people around them would know that they were educated.

It was fun, too, watching a funny little man with a funny little mustache and a funny derby hat and funny, baggy pants earn himself a million dollars, tax free. So it was no wonder that Charlie Chaplin became a national hero as he rolled to fame on a wave of two-reelers. Yet, certainly nobody in that era would have dreamed of linking their favorite funny man with anything that even slightly resembled international intrigue. Charlie's nearest approach to espionage was in a picture called *Shoulder Arms* in which he was camouflaged as a tree, in the No-Man's-Land of World War I.

But a dozen years later, the plot began to thicken. By then, Charlie had hired a Japanese valet, which wasn't surprising. Many people were hiring Japanese valets because they were so efficient. Some of the valets worked very cheaply, too, for little more than expenses. They could

69

afford it, as they were collecting their real salaries from the Japanese Army and Navy, which had assigned them to special service.

When Charlie Chaplin made a world tour in 1932, his valet, whose name was Kono, preceded him to Japan and arranged a grand welcome. In Tokyo, Kono himself rose into prominence by saving Charlie from assassination by a war party that wanted to provoke an international incident. How far Kono may have appeased the secret agents is still a question, but apparently they settled by assassinating the Japanese premier, Ki Inukai, instead of the visiting movie star.

This brief brush with the cloak-and-dagger set is covered in Chaplin's *My Autobiography*, but with the conclusion of the episode, Kono drops abruptly from its pages. That is unfortunate, as readers might well be interested in learning what happened to Kono afterward.

If you are so inclined, read on. For Kono's subsequent history has long been a matter of official record woven into the fabric of the true tale that follows, as related by that prince of factual narrators, Alan Hynd.

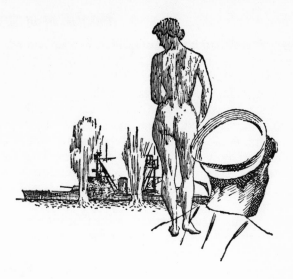

Encounter at
Treasure Island

ALAN HYND

AT the San Francisco World's Fair in 1940, one of the exhibits was called the Candid Camera Artists' Models Studio. It was quite a drawing card, for men with candid cameras could purchase admission to the exhibit, where they found several specialists in pulchritude posing in the nude. Just what percentage of men who had no interest whatsoever in photographic work purchased candid cameras to get into the show and look over the subjects is perhaps beside the point. For that nude exhibit happened to serve as the background for the beginning of one of the most fabulous spy plots of modern times.

One of the owners of the exhibit was a former vaudeville performer named Al Blake—an alert-looking, nattily attired man with sharp eyes and a trim mustache. Blake was now in middle age, but he had always taken excellent care

71

of himself and had the physique of a man considerably younger. At one time, Blake had been known as the King of the Robots. He had performed in vaudeville and in department store windows. He possessed the gift of remarkable control over his voluntary and involuntary muscles. Sometimes for hours on end, with a waxlike makeup applied to his face, he would stand in a department store window, alongside a dummy dressed exactly like him. The idea was for those in the crowd in front of the window to decide which was Blake and which was the dummy. It wasn't an easy matter.

Blake's background is important in that his control over his voluntary and involuntary muscles was to be of vital importance to the United States of America in the years 1940 and 1941. On a day in the fall of 1940 a squat little Japanese, with a candid camera on a leather strap around his neck, walked into the Artists' Models Studio. With the eye of the connoisseur, the Japanese looked over the girls, photographed them, and then glanced around at others in the place, just out of a natural curiosity characteristically Japanese. Thus it was that his eyes met those of Al Blake, the so-called King of the Robots. The face of the Japanese creased in a smile and he approached Blake with outstretched hand and said, "How are you? Don't you remember me?"

Blake didn't. Whereupon the Japanese explained that he was Torzichi Kono, one-time valet, chauffeur, and general handyman for Charlie Chaplin. Yes, Blake did recall him now. His mind flashed back to 1917, when he had first met Kono in the Chaplin studio in Hollywood. Blake had played a small part in Chaplin's classic war comedy, *Shoulder Arms*. There had been a well-remembered scene in a trench where the water rose higher and higher and gradually submerged Chaplin's bunk, the lower one. Al Blake, who was running the nude show at Treasure Island almost a quarter of a century later, had been the man in the upper bunk.

There was something vague and mysterious about Kono's

behavior that intrigued Blake. The thought crossed Blake's mind that maybe Kono was a Japanese spy, but he told himself that he was too quick to suspect every Japanese of being a spy. Then, after a few moments of general conversation, Blake became suspicious of Kono for a second time when the Japanese said, "Say, Blake, you used to be in the Navy, didn't you?"

Blake nodded. "Yes," he said, "in the last war. I was a yeoman." He wondered how Kono knew that about him.

"Too bad you're not in the Navy now," said Kono. "You could make a lot of money."

Kono walked out of Blake's exhibit, and that was the last the King of the Robots saw of him again until one day in March of the following year—1941. Blake was walking along Santa Monica Boulevard in Hollywood, where he lived, when he met Kono by accident. Since the previous fall, the thought of Kono's suspicious behavior at the Treasure Island exhibit had intrigued Blake.

This time Blake was all ready with just what to say. After the opening pleasantries and a little general talk, Blake remarked, "I'm thinking of joining the Navy again if they'll have me."

Kono seemed interested. "It's a great life, the Navy," he said.

"Yeah," said Blake. "I just heard from a friend of mine in the Navy the other day. He's stationed out in Hawaii, the lucky dog."

"On what ship?" asked Kono.

"The *Pennsylvania*. The flagship."

"Look," said Kono, "if you're going in the Navy again, Blake, or even if you're not but have a friend on the flagship, maybe I can show you how to make a lot of money."

"God knows I could use some money," said Blake, who was actually quite solvent. "The finance company's after me about my car."

Kono's eyes glittered. He was obviously pleased to hear that Blake was in financial distress. He insisted that Blake mark down his Hollywood address and telephone number. "Maybe," said Kono, "you would like to be my guest at dinner. I have some things I would like to talk over with you. I think they would be to mutual advantage."

Kono took Blake's telephone number before the two parted. Later, he phoned Blake and invited him to dinner at a Japanese restaurant in Hollywood. After footing the bill for an elaborate repast, Kono got down to brass tacks.

"About this friend you say you have in the Navy, Al— this man on the *Pennsylvania*—could you get in touch with him any time?" Kono asked.

"Sure. Jimmie Campbell and I are old buddies. We correspond frequently."

The name and the person were purely fictitious, having been thought up by Blake for the occasion. But, as was to turn out later, the fictitious man and the fictitious name were to become very real and to play a major role in Uncle Sam's fight against the Japanese Secret Service.

Kono arranged other meetings with Blake and sounded him out further. Finally, he was fully satisfied, and stated: "At noon tomorrow be at the corner of Sunset Boulevard and Wilton Street out in Hollywood. A very important man will be there to talk to you."

The next day Blake was at the appointed street corner right on the stroke of twelve. He found Kono waiting. The Japanese was smoking a cigarette and his hat brim was pulled low over his brow as if he didn't want anyone to recognize him. When Blake approached, Kono made a surreptitious gesture that clearly indicated that he did not wish Blake to begin talking with him, but rather to remain near so that the two would give the appearance that they were not together but just standing there waiting for a bus.

Presently a sedan drew up to the curb. A Japanese was at the wheel. Without looking at Kono, the man at the wheel reached into the back of the car and opened the rear right door. Kono hurried into the car and then motioned to

Blake to get into the back seat with him. Then the machine spurted off. It went into the Hollywood hills, and during a ride of about fifteen minutes not a word was spoken by any of the three occupants. The driver seemed to be a man of about thirty-five, and on the fat side. When at length the car stopped in a desolate spot, he said to Kono, "Introduce me to your friend." There followed a formal introduction that seemed rather ludicrous to Blake.

During the introduction, it developed that the driver called himself Mr. Yamato. He got right down to business. "Mr. Blake," he said, "tell me something about this friend of yours—this Jimmie Campbell, the yeoman on the *Pennsylvania.*"

Blake began to get cagey. He wanted something a little more definite from the Japanese before he went deeper into the deal. He turned to Kono. "Who is Mr. Yamato, anyway, Kono?" he asked. "I'm being asked a lot of questions here, and I don't know what it's all about." Blake paused briefly, then went on. "That is, I've got a pretty good idea what it's about, and I'm willing to string along. But there's got to be definite arrangements—particularly about dough."

Kono looked at Yamato in a subservient sort of way. During all this time the latter had not turned to look at either Kono or Blake, but had used the rear vision mirror to watch the facial expressions of the men in the back seat when he talked to them.

The driver was silent for a few moments. Then he said to Blake, "Would you be prepared to leave for Hawaii, Mr. Blake?"

"I'll leave for Tibet if there's enough money in it," said Blake.

"Mr. Kono will attend to all of the financial details, Mr. Blake," answered Mr. Yamato. "You needn't worry about expenses or remuneration. Be assured you will be treated very well."

"But just what am I to do?" asked Blake. "Have I got it

straight that I am to be a spy and to get this friend of mine on the *Pennsylvania* to get information for the Japanese Government?"

"You have the general idea, Mr. Blake. Be ready to leave for Hawaii at any time. Now, where shall we drop you?"

Blake suggested a bowling alley on Sunset Boulevard. Once there, he ducked out of a rear exit to a corner where he caught a bus for Los Angeles. He wanted to go to the Office of Naval Intelligence and apprise the authorities of what was going on. But when he looked back, Blake saw that the bus was being trailed by a car containing two Japanese!

So Blake postponed his trip to the O.N.I. Instead, he went in and out of a Los Angeles department store, only to find the car waiting when he came out, so he went into a motion picture theater. Even in the darkness of the theater, he couldn't shake off the Japanese. One of them sat only two rows behind him, and the other across the aisle. When the show was over, Blake called it a day and returned to his Hollywood apartment.

As Blake sat in his apartment thinking things over, his eye suddenly fell on a patch of the rug in his living room that somehow appeared unnatural. There was an indentation in the rug, as if made by a piece of furniture that had long stood in one place but had been moved. The piece of furniture obviously was a heavy chair which had indeed been shifted. There should have been no one in his apartment that day, but apparently someone had been there.

He approached the chair cautiously and examined it. Just as he thought, he came upon a dictograph, planted under one of the arms. The Japanese had removed the cloth covering of the arm and sewed it back on again. The wire attached to the dictograph had then been put through a tiny hole made in the rug beneath the chair, and run under the rug and through a hole in the baseboard of the wall. From that point it had obviously followed the telephone wires outside, and it was not possible for Blake to find out just then whether the listening device on the other end of the apparatus was in the same building or some distance away.

Not long after Blake made the discovery of the dictograph, his telephone rang. Mr. Kono was on the wire. "That was a good meeting we had today, Al," said Kono. "The driver of the car was very impressed by you; he likes you very much."

"I'm glad of that, Kono," said Al. "Where do we go from here?"

"You'll be hearing from me in the morning."

Kono phoned again the next morning and another meeting was arranged with Mr. Yamato. At the second conference of the three men in the Hollywood hills, the two Japanese talked in their native tongue for a while, then Yamato said to Blake, "Are you prepared to leave within a week by Clipper for Honolulu?" Blake nodded. "Mr. Kono here," Yamato went on, "will give you full instructions about just what we want when you get there. But to give you a general idea now, you are to see your friend, Jimmie Campbell, as soon as you can after your arrival and make the proper arrangements to get everything that will be of value to the Imperial Japanese Government—such things as codes that the Navy uses, all tactical information, charts of mine fields, and so on."

"What about money?" asked Blake.

"How much do you want?" said Kono.

"Twenty-five hundred down and all expenses," said Blake, "and five thousand more when I deliver."

"That's exactly the figure we had in mind," said Yamato, and Blake had to call upon his ability to control his involuntary muscles in order to keep from laughing at the obvious lie. For Yamato was apparently pleased to hear Blake's figure—a lower one than he had expected him to demand.

That afternoon Blake decided that he would simply have to get in touch with the O.N.I. Once more he headed into

Los Angeles by bus, but once more the car with the two
trailing Japanese was right behind. This time Blake went
right for a motion picture theater. Inasmuch as he had
stayed through the entire show the last time he had been
followed by the Japanese, he figured on the possibility of the
Japanese not following him into the playhouse but waiting
outside until the show was over. As luck would have it, they
parked in the car across from the theater and did not get
out.

Blake had a talk with the manager inside the darkened
theater, told him he was being followed, and asked if he
could be let out another exit that would give him access to a
different street. The manager was willing to oblige him and
Blake was soon outside. He walked back to a point that
afforded a view of the front of the theater and saw the two
Japanese still sitting in the car, apparently quite content
to wait until he came out to pick him up.

When Blake reached the O.N.I. and made it clear to an
officer there that he had information of a vital nature, he
was shown into the office of Lieutenant Leo P. Stanley of
the United States Naval Intelligence. Blake told his story in
a simple straightforward manner and Stanley never interrupted to say a single word while the narrative was in progress. After Blake had finished, Lieutenant Stanley said,
"This sounds very important, Mr. Blake. And it also sounds
as if you have to do exactly as the Japanese say."

"How do you mean, Lieutenant?" asked Blake.

"Ordinarily," said Lieutenant Stanley, "a private citizen
who turns in information such as this no longer has to be
concerned with the outcome because experts in the field of
investigation follow through. But in this instance, you will
have to carry the ball for us, for it simply wouldn't be possible for us to work things so that anyone could substitute
for you."

"You mean that you have no intention of arresting Kono
and this Mr. Yamato?"

"None whatever at present," said Lieutenant Stanley. "Incidentally, before I forget it, I must warn you that an associate of Kono's has planted a dictograph in your apartment in Hollywood."

Blake, startled, inquired how Stanley knew that. "Simply because we have had an eye on Kono and his associates for some time. You see, the fact that you, Mr. Blake, possess the singular ability to control both your voluntary and involuntary muscles is one of the reasons why the Japanese sought you out in the first place. They wish to get a white spy who will have such superb control over himself that he will not betray himself in a tight spot. We intend to use that very quality of yours against the Japanese."

While Blake was growing more astonished over Stanley's knowledge of facts which Blake thought only he himself knew about, the O.N.I. officer consulted some papers on his desk. "We can't be too long with our meeting today," Stanley said as he looked through the papers, "because you will have to get back to the theater before the show ends. Otherwise, the two Japanese in the car outside the theater will get suspicious."

At this Blake was more astonished than ever. He had not mentioned a word to Lieutenant Stanley about where he had been prior to reaching the O.N.I. offices. So he asked, "How did you know about that, Lieutenant?"

Stanley smiled. "We have been following you, as well as those who have followed you, ever since that day last year at Treasure Island when Kono walked into your exhibit. The very fact that you came here voluntarily and informed me of many things we already knew, in addition to many things we did not know—such as the nature of the conversations you had with Kono and Commander Tachibana in the Hollywood hills—proves your good faith."

"Commander Tachibana?" Blake repeated. "That's a new name on me. The man I spoke to with Kono was named Yamato."

"To be sure," said Lieutenant Stanley. "That's the name that has been assumed by Commander Itaru Tachibana of the Japanese Navy. We have known about the Commander for some time. It is important that you should know something about his background." Whereupon Lieutenant Stanley divulged the information they had about the man who called himself Yamato.

Stanley went on to explain that the O.N.I. would follow through on Blake's bright idea of having thought up a fictitious yeoman on the *Pennsylvania*. When Blake asked how, the lieutenant explained, "We will put an operative on the *Pennsylvania*. He will be dressed as a yeoman and he will answer to the name of Jimmie Campbell." Stanley laughed. "So you see there actually will be such a person as Jimmie Campbell in the event that the Japanese in Hawaii should go to the trouble of checking up. Moreover, if you are instructed to write to this man and let him know of your coming, the letter will be delivered. It wouldn't be a very good thing, you know, if you sent a letter and had it returned for lack of an addressee, for the Japanese are unquestionably watching your mail." Stanley looked at the clock. "Mr. Blake," he said, "you had better be getting back to the theater. I assume you will have no trouble getting in the same way you came out?"

"No trouble at all," said Blake. "The manager's a very nice guy. When do you want me to get in touch with you again?"

"You are not to come here again. It's too dangerous. You will be contacted at the proper time and told what to do. Meanwhile, do as the Japanese say."

Blake inquired as to what the set-up was to be in Honolulu. Stanley replied that details would have to be perfected, but that he would receive instructions in good time.

That night Kono telephoned to Blake. "Start making your reservation for Honolulu, Al," said the Japanese. "Leave tomorrow by Clipper if you can."

Blake immediately telephoned to Pan-Pacific Air Lines.

He was told that all space was sold out for two weeks. Actually, it wasn't, but the Navy needed time to make proper preparations in Honolulu. O.N.I. officers knew that in addition to the dictograph, Blake's phone was also tapped, and they figured that if the Japanese heard a false report that Clipper space was unobtainable, they would accept the delay.

Instead, the Japanese decided that Blake should take a steamer from San Francisco, the coming Saturday. The O.N.I overheard that, but let it go through, as it allowed them ample time. On Friday night, Kono drove Blake to the Union Passenger Terminal in Los Angeles. Just before the midnight train for San Francisco pulled out, Kono handed Blake an envelope.

"There's a couple of thousand dollars in here," he said. "That will cover your expenses."

In San Francisco, Blake embarked for Honolulu on the *President Garfield* of the Dollar Line. They were hardly through the Golden Gate before Blake discovered that two gentlemen of Teutonic appearance shared the cabin to the forward side of his, and two Japanese occupied the adjoining cabin to his aft.

All four hovered about the bar when Blake had some drinks there. Later, Blake checked the passenger list in the purser's office and found that both Germans were going under the name of Mueller, which is as common as Smith or Jones in the United States. Obviously, those names were assumed, which confirmed Blake's suspicion that the Germans were secret agents operating on behalf of the Japanese Government.

For three days and three nights, Blake knew that he was under the constant surveillance of either the two Japanese or the Messrs. Mueller. He had become so adjusted to the situation by this time, however, that he was able to ignore it. He thoroughly enjoyed himself by playing shuffleboard and bingo and otherwise participating in the diversions offered on an ocean trip. Blake was a good mixer and he struck up friendships all over the ship, but his closest was with an elderly American and his wife.

The American's name was Horner, and he said he was a hardware dealer from the Middle West. Among other things, Mr. Horner, as everybody on the ship knew, was constantly expecting a radiogram. His daughter, he had announced, was about to have a baby and the news as to whether the child was a boy or a girl was to be radioed to the Horners immediately.

It wasn't until the last night out that Mr. Horner received his radiogram. It was quite a long message of its kind, announcing that the baby was a boy and giving the child's weight, the name that had been conferred upon it, who the officiating doctor had been, and other such details. Mr. Horner showed the message to many of the passengers, including the younger Mr. Mueller and both of the Japanese. Then, by way of celebration, he set up drinks for everybody who would accept and was soon quite obviously roaring drunk.

Al Blake was in the Horner party, and finally Mrs. Horner, patently quite embarrassed by her husband's behavior, appealed to Blake to assist her in getting the old boy to his stateroom.

Blake had quite a struggle. Horner resented the interruption to his gaiety and took a swing at Blake, giving the King of the Robots quite a cut under the eye. Blake, angered, wanted nothing further to do with Horner, but the old man's wife pleaded for aid.

Finally Blake got Horner to his stateroom. The old man bellowed for his radiogram, which he had dropped during the scuffle in the bar, and insisted that Mrs. Horner go and hunt for it. When his wife left, Horner startled Blake by seeming to sober suddenly. "Lock the door," he whispered to Blake. The King of the Robots complied mechanically. By the time he had locked the door and turned around, old Horner had arisen from the bed, where a few minutes before he had appeared to be quite the worse for alcohol. Now he was steady, grim, and clear-eyed. "Blake," he said, "I have your instructions for you."

"Oh," said Blake. "You're——?"

Horner interrupted by nodding affirmatively, "I'll have to talk fast," he said, "as you'll have to get back to the bar or they'll get suspicious." Blake was reaching into his pocket for pencil and paper. "No," said Horner, "no notes. Just listen: The radiogram I just received contained your instructions." The instructions were that upon his arrival in his Honolulu hotel, Blake was immediately to put through a call for the U.S.S. *Pennsylvania,* which was anchored at Pearl Harbor, and ask to speak to Yeoman Jimmie Campbell—the counter-espionage agent O.N.I. had planted on the ship. "Our people in Honolulu have found out certain things since this ship left San Francisco," Horner explained. "The Japanese there have arranged that you be assigned to a certain room when you register at the hotel. You are going to be watched very closely while you are in that room. For one thing, the two Japanese who are next to you on this ship will be in a room adjoining yours at the hotel. The two Germans on the other side of you on this ship will be on the other side of you at the hotel."

"That's not very smart of them, is it," asked Blake, "having the same men who flanked me on the ship doing the same thing at the hotel?"

Horner shook his head sideways and smiled. "No, it isn't," he said, "but you'll find as you go along that despite their cleverness the Japanese can be stupid, too. For one thing, I think it was unnecessary for them to have had you under surveillance during this trip, just to see whether you intend to double-cross them or not. Certainly you couldn't have done much double-crossing here. But to get on. In addition to the eavesdroppers on either side of you in the hotel, there will be a dictograph planted in your room. It has, in fact, already been placed there. It is concealed behind the blind in the upper right-hand corner of the left-hand window in your room—left-hand as you look out.

Make certain that most of your conversations with Yeoman Campbell are conducted near the spot."

"When I call Campbell," asked Blake, "what shall I say?"

"Just be natural. Don't have anything made up beforehand. Just act as if Campbell is an old buddy of yours that you haven't seen for some time. Ask him what he's doing and when he can get away for you two to meet."

"And where are we to meet?"

"He'll come to your room. You'll feel him out as to how satisfied he is with life in the Navy, and he'll tell you he's disgruntled—so disgruntled in fact, that that will be your opening to put your proposition to him. He will carry on from there, for the benefit of the spies in the adjoining rooms and for members of the Japanese Secret Service in another part of the hotel who will be listening in over the dictograph. Just remember, all you have to do is to act natural. You are trying to get information from Campbell for the Japanese government and the money that the Japanese are willing to pay for it will benefit both of you."

"Is Campbell going to go for this in a big way?" asked Blake.

"Yes and no," said Horner. "He will act natural, too. The stumbling block, so far as he is concerned, will be the possibility of his getting caught. You are to be a parrot and repeat what the Japanese have told you to say if he should be afraid."

"Am I to get all of my instructions through Campbell?"

"Yes," answered Horner. "He will either gesture to you or show you things in writing when you are in your hotel room with him." Horner was undressed by this time and he got back on his bed and into his drunken stupor pose. He came out of the pose long enough to grasp Blake's hand firmly, and say, "Good luck, Blake."

Blake followed instructions to the letter, calling Yeoman Campbell on the *Pennsylvania* at Pearl Harbor. An appointment was made for Campbell to call at Blake's hotel room that night, and he showed up right on the dot. Campbell was a big, hard man of over forty, and he certainly looked the part he was to play, even to the color and texture of his skin, which was tanned and wind-beaten.

The intelligence operative and Al Blake went into a long-lost brother routine for the benefit of the eavesdroppers in the adjoining rooms and the Japanese listening at the other end of the dictograph. The O.N.I. was listening in, too. If the Japanese could plant a "bug" in Blake's room, so could Uncle Sam's agents.

Campbell asked, "What brings you out here anyway, Al?"

"Something that might be worth a lot of dough to both of us, Jimmie," said Blake.

"How do you mean dough? I could use some."

"Couldn't we all?" countered Blake. "But first of all, Jimmie, how are you getting along in the Navy?"

"Listen," said Campbell, "here I've been in this damned outfit since the last war—when we were in together, Al—and where the hell am I? I'll tell you where I am: I'm beneath a lot of punks that came in after I did and got shoved ahead of me."

"You don't sound very patriotic, Jimmie," said Blake with a laugh.

"Patriotic, hell!"

"Well, look," said Blake. "This is going to make things easier for me. I came out here with a proposition for you, but I figured I might have to sell you on it a little. But now that I see how things are it should be a cinch."

Blake took Campbell by the arm and steered him to a point just under the dictograph—perfectly normal behavior under the circumstances, inasmuch as anyone who did not wish to be overheard would be likely to step toward a window rather than toward a wall or a door. Now Blake began to put the Japanese proposition up to the man whom the listeners thought was a yeoman on the *Pennsylvania*. The King of the Robots talked in a low tone that was just loud enough to be picked up by the delicate dictograph above his head, and then amplified as much as necessary in the room where the Japanese Secret Service operatives were stationed.

The strategy was for Blake to request all the information that he sought of Campbell without stating whom he wanted it for and without being interrupted while he was talking. It took Blake about ten minutes to speak his piece. Then Campbell said, "Who you working for, Al—the Japs?"

"Yes."

Now the strategy called for Campbell to say that while he didn't like the United States Navy he didn't like the Japs either. The O.N.I. had decided that a note of realism and authenticity would be added if the Japs overheard themselves being spoken of in an unfavorable way. Carrying out this idea still further, Blake added, "Well, dough's dough, no matter where you get it. There's a lot of things about the Japs I'm not nuts about either, Jimmie, but what the hell, if you can make a deal with them, well and good."

The strategy now called for some silence, during which Campbell was to pace up and down the room, as if debating with himself. He paced heavily enough for the dictograph to pick up the sounds of his footfalls. Then he rejoined Blake under the dictograph and said, "This stuff I'm supposed to get—codes and so on—what would happen if the big boys on the *Pennsylvania* missed it?"

"You don't understand, Jimmie," said Blake. "You're only supposed to borrow it or copy it. You've got all the chance in the world to do that. It would never be missed. And anyway, suppose the worst happened and it was missed, how could they pin it on you? Why, any one of a *hundred* guys could have taken it."

When Campbell was about to leave, the arrangement was that he would come to Blake's room again the next night. But here again the O.N.I. resorted to some psychology. They wanted everything to appear perfectly natural. Had things gone too smoothly or too easily for Blake, the Japanese might have become suspicious. So Campbell telephoned to Blake the following night an hour before he was due. He knew that every word he said over the phone would be heard by the Japanese, for the O.N.I. had in the meantime learned that Blake's phone had been tapped. Campbell said that he couldn't get off the ship that night, and that he would make it the following night. Blake, trying to appear as anxious as became anyone on so serious a mission, inquired, "Anything doing on that matter I spoke to you about, Jimmie?"

"So long, Al, see you tomorrow night," snapped Campbell, as if he were afraid to talk.

When Campbell put in his second appearance at Blake's hotel room but one thought seemed uppermost in his mind —the possibility of getting caught. Blake argued the matter under the dictograph for almost half an hour, and finally seemed to persuade Campbell that it would be safe enough for him to go ahead. Up to this time not a word had been said about the ease or difficulty with which Campbell could obtain the desired information, but the inference was that the espionage itself would be quite easy. Now Blake brought up the matter. "Hell," answered Campbell, "it's a lead-pipe cinch. So far as laying my hands on the stuff you want, it's like taking candy from a kid. The only thing that bothers me is that something could go wrong somewhere."

Campbell had made it a practice to stop at a certain bar in downtown Honolulu after leaving Blake's room. Blake put through a telephone call for the bar and reached the intelligence officer. "I've got good news for you, Jimmie," he said, "if you can come right back. Something immediate."

When Campbell returned and Blake gave him one thousand dollars, the intelligence man promised to get right to work. "For a few more of these, Al," he said, "I'll turn over the whole God damned fleet."

From that point on, the negotiations proceeded smoothly. Bit by bit, Campbell turned over to the King of the Robots one of the most stunning collections of spurious information ever designed by one great world power to mislead

another one. A great deal of thought had gone into the information Blake was to take back with him. Naval Intelligence operatives knew that the Japanese were well acquainted with certain supposedly closely kept secrets relating to the United States Navy. It would never have done,
then, to have concocted information that was too far from
the truth; it would have been spotted for what it was immediately. The problem had been to steer a middle course
wherein the information would appear to be accurate but
would in reality be dangerously inaccurate.

Kono and Commander Tachibana received Blake with
open arms upon his return to Hollywood. Tachibana was
particularly excited about what Blake had brought back.
He spoke vaguely of big things for Blake in the future.
But he was immediately concerned by something else—a
quick return trip by Blake to Honolulu.

Blake inquired of Commander Tachibana the reason for
the return trip to Honolulu since he had just come back
loaded down with what the Japanese spy unquestionably regarded as vital information. Tachibana replied that Blake
would be secretly instructed by an attaché of the Japanese
Consulate in the Hawaiian city upon his return there. While
he was talking to Blake, Tachibana glanced at Kono, and
there was something in the glance that caused Blake to become apprehensive about his personal safety.

Blake brought up the question of money and Tachibana
showed a desire to haggle. He said he would have to examine Blake's information more thoroughly before he could
determine just how much it was worth to the Japanese Government.

The next day Blake left his apartment in Hollywood and
took a bus for Los Angeles with the intention of going to
the offices of the O.N.I. and reporting to Lieutenant
Stanley. Again, a car with two Japanese was following the
bus. In accordance with special instructions, Blake went
straight to a movie theater that Stanley had designated.
Waiting inside was an operative of the O.N.I. made up to

look almost exactly like Blake. He pointed Blake to a side exit and from there, the Robot King watched the Jap agents enter from the lobby and follow his double down the aisle and take seats two rows behind him. That left Blake free to continue on his way to O.N.I. headquarters.

There, Stanley was most interested in the plan of Commander Tachibana to have Blake return to the Islands. Stanley thought briefly about the matter when Blake mentioned it to him, then left the room to confer with other intelligence officers. When he returned, his face was grave. "Blake," he said. "I might as well be frank with you. They are asking you to go back to Honolulu for the purpose of killing you there."

"How do you figure that?" asked the King of the Robots, who was living up to his name, for no suggestion of fear showed in his face.

"Their psychology would be this, Blake. Your usefulness to them is over. As long as you live you will be a potential menace to them. It's the old story of dead men telling no tales. While I am certain that they have not caught on to what you are really doing, they themselves have no assurance that you will not eventually run afoul of our organization or of the F.B.I. And if you were ever picked up, the Japanese would figure that you might talk."

"I think as much of my neck as the next man," said Blake, "and naturally I don't want to stick it out for a Japanese axe. But tell me this, Lieutenant: Could I accomplish anything worthwhile for the United States Government if I returned to Hawaii as they want me to?"

Stanley gazed out of the window for what seemed to Blake to be an interminably long time before answering. When he spoke, he said, "That's just the point, Blake. You can render your greatest service on this second trip."

Blake wanted to know how. "You said that Tachibana told you that an attaché of the Japanese Consulate in Honolulu would look after you this time," said Stanley. "All right. We need such a contact but haven't been able to effect one so far. If you were to go out there and establish such a connection it might be possible for you to get hold of some vital information for us." Again Blake asked, "How?"

Lieutenant Stanley gave the details. Blake was again to establish a rendezvous with the operative posing as Yeoman Jimmie Campbell, who was to stumble across new and apparently vital information. Blake was to mention this to the attaché of the Consulate, so the Japanese would give him a reprieve until after he turned over this latest intelligence.

Meanwhile, Blake was to learn how much the Japanese knew about other vital naval secrets by observing the intensity of their reactions to the information that he gave them.

"For more than a year now," Stanley explained, "we have had the data all prepared to be tested on the Japanese, but we have never managed to maneuver things so that we could get an American to put it up to them without arousing their suspicions."

Lieutenant Stanley lapsed into silence again. Then he said, "That's how things are, Blake. Understand, there's no guarantee that the Japanese will go for this bait. All we could guarantee, if you return to Hawaii, would be the closest shave you've ever had in your life; that is, if you don't actually get killed. Still want to go?"

The very least that can be said for Al Blake is that he was a patriot. Moreover, he had come to despise the Japanese thoroughly through association with them. Thus he was motivated by personal feelings as well as patriotism. "Sure as hell I want to go," he said.

"Hadn't you better think it over for a day or two, Blake?"

"I've been thinking it over all the time I've been here, Lieutenant," said the King of the Robots. "When I make up my mind, I make it up—and it's made up."

Lieutenant Stanley provided Blake with more than thirty apparent vital facts relating to naval operations. These were the half truths and three-quarter truths that the

O.N.I. had prepared for one day getting Japanese reactions to them. Blake was to memorize them and supposedly come across the bait data through Yeoman Campbell. The two were to do no talking in Blake's quarters on this trip. Blake was to tell Campbell that he was afraid American agents might be listening.

The O.N.I. subterfuge in the theater worked perfectly on Blake's way home. Blake came in through the side exit and switched with the masquerader when he was coming out to the lobby. Blake was then tailed by the Japanese back to his Hollywood apartment.

Not thirty-six hours after he had received instructions from Lieutenant Stanley, Blake found himself on an overnight limited from Los Angeles to San Francisco, from which point he was, on the day of his arrival, to take a steamer for the islands. Just before his departure on the liner, Blake was approached at the pier by a little Japanese he had never seen before. He was given instructions on what hotel to stay at when he reached Honolulu, and also informed that he was not to leave his hotel room under any circumstances until he had received word of some kind from an attaché of the Japanese Consulate. Blake asked what he was supposed to do about food.

"Order your meals served in your room," was the answer.

Blake was two days at sea when he arrived at the definite conclusion that there were no shadows aboard ship. This was further indication to him, if he needed any, that so far as the Japanese was concerned, he was sailing to his death.

On arrival at Honolulu, when he checked into the hotel —not the same hotel he had previously stopped at—he found that a dictograph was planted in the room. This time the "bug" was not behind a blind, but was concealed inside a secret compartment of a small writing desk.

The Japanese had not instructed Blake against communicating with Yeoman Campbell, so he called the U.S.S. *Pennsylvania* and got the intelligence operative on the

phone. Proceeding on the theory that his telephone had
been tapped again, Blake spoke with that in mind, and so
did Campbell. The supposed yeoman was all for meeting
Blake at once, mentioning, in guarded language, the fact
that he was anxious to get the remainder of his pay for the
data that he had previously turned over to Blake. The King
of the Robots, mindful of the fact that the Japanese had
told him not to leave his room until he received a communication from a consular attaché, stalled Campbell along,
explaining that he would give him another ring when it
was all right to come to the hotel. "I can explain everything
when I see you, Jimmie," said Blake. "In the meantime,
you've got to trust me."

Campbell sounded very suspicious about the fact that
Blake was in Honolulu again and that there would be a
delay in the two of them getting together. The O.N.I. had
decided that this reaction on Campbell's part would sound
like normal behavior by a person who had turned over valuable confidential data, expecting to be paid for it. Anything
that could be done further to convince the Japanese that Al
Blake had been absolutely on the level with them was considered of paramount importance. No matter what else happened, it was vital that the Japanese should regard the information that Blake had already turned over as being authentic
in every respect. Naturally, in the summer of 1941—almost
half a year before Pearl Harbor—American realists in high
places did not know just when, where or how a Japanese attack would come—but they knew it would come. And they
were preparing for it so that when the attack was made Japan
would be acting on certain false information—the information that had been planted on the Imperial Japanese Government through the medium of Al Blake.

On the second day of Blake's return visit to Honolulu
there was a faint tapping on the door of his hotel room in
midafternon. Blake opened the door to find a smiling
young Japanese, faultlessly tailored in white linen, at the

threshold. "Good afternoon, Mr. Blake," said the visitor, stepping inside without waiting for an invitation.

The man identified himself as a consular attaché but did not give his name. Without preliminaries, he got right to the business at hand. He told Blake just what would be expected of him during his sojourn on the islands. He would be required to get in touch again with his friend, Yeoman Campbell of the U.S.S. *Pennsylvania,* with the idea of having Campbell arrange things so that Blake could go out to Pearl Harbor and make certain observations at certain locations where men with yellow faces couldn't go without arousing the suspicion of the naval authorities.

When Blake asked for details of what he was to observe, the Japanese brought out a little book and consulted it. He thereupon took some stationery from Blake's desk and drew diagrams of certain locations at Pearl Harbor. Among other things, Blake had been made acquainted with information such as this in order that he would be able to evaluate Japanese moves as he went along. Thus it was that when his visitor told him just what it was he wanted him to observe at Pearl Harbor, Blake had further evidence that the sole motive of the Japanese in getting him to Hawaii for the second time was to kill him.

For, in the first place, the observations that the visitor asked him to make were of the most innocuous sort—the type of thing that would have little or no intelligence value, and certainly hardly the kind of information that would have warranted the Japanese bringing Blake all the way from the mainland to obtain. If the Japanese were not indeed already in possession of the information that the little man in the linen suit was asking Blake to get, it would have been comparatively simple to obtain by more than one means. But in order to get the information, it would be necessary for Blake to go out to Pearl Harbor. Such a trip entailed passing over certain stretches of lonely territory that lay between the hotel and the naval base—territory where it would be ideal for killers to wait in ambush until their victim came along.

After his visitor left, Blake phoned Campbell, who came to the hotel room and demanded to know where his money was. When Blake stated that the Japanese were trying to arrive at a fair figure for the data, Campbell went into a tirade, calling the Japanese every unprintable name that he could lay his tongue on. Campbell finished with the remark:

"But I was smarter than they were. They didn't get one-tenth of what I got my hands on. Take a look at this!" The operative rustled some sheets of perfectly blank paper on the desk where the dictograph was planted. To those listening at the other end, it sounded as if Blake were really looking at some extremely valuable information.

"Well, for God's sake!" Blake would say at appropriate intervals. Then, finally, "Jimmie, look—will you let me have some of this stuff to take back?"

Campbell was adamant. "Nuts to that. I want to see the color of their dough before I let this stuff go."

An hour after Campbell left, the Japanese attaché called on Blake, ostensibly to go over some minor details. About to leave, he queried, "Would it be possible to obtain some additional information such as Mr. Campbell gave you on your last visit?"

Blake shook his head emphatically at that.

"We'll just have to get some dough, or at least some assurance as to what the eventual price is going to be. If that can be arranged, I don't mind telling you that I'll be in a position to get some of the damnedest stuff for you that you've ever even thought of."

As if he didn't know what Blake was driving at, the Japanese asked for details. "I don't know the details, as a matter of fact," said Blake. "I didn't have long enough to study the stuff. Campbell had it with him when he was here and he let me see just enough of it to know that it's practically priceless. I hate to admit it, because it makes me out a sort of a dope, but the guy held out on me when I was here before. I figured I had got everything he had, but he was a little too cagey for that, and I went back with only a fraction of what's available."

The Japanese was obviously in deep thought when he departed. Early the next morning he was back at Blake's room again. He handed the American an envelope. "There's three thousand dollars in there in American cash," he explained. "Give it to your friend Campbell, and have him turn over to you some of this new information." While Blake was counting the money, the Japanese said, "To use an American expression, that will be but a drop in the bucket compared to what you and Campbell will get if this information turns out as good as it promises to be."

In the ensuing several days, Blake turned over the Campbell information bit by bit. Keeping his face as expressionless as possible, he studied the expression on the face of the Japanese as the information was turned over. Blake was well aware of the fact that the Japanese were similar to him in that one way—they were able to mask their inner feelings, as a rule. However, the intensity of interest that shone from the eyes of the consular attaché as he examined the spurious information was a definite tip-off to Blake that the newest Campbell data were going to be regarded as of paramount importance in Jap quarters.

Al Blake had been in Honolulu for almost two weeks of his second visit when the man posing as Yeoman Campbell of the U.S.S. *Pennsylvania* called at his room one night and, while greeting Blake in routine fashion for the benefit of the Japanese listening in on the dictograph, held up a note saying:

I am going to suggest that we go out together. Pretend that you don't feel good and don't want to go, but agree with me in the end and come with me.

There now started a conversation along the lines outlined in the note, and in a little while Blake and Campbell left for a Honolulu hot spot. Campbell had mentioned the name of the place that he wanted to take Blake to, so that the Japanese would send shadow men there rather than put tails on the Americans at the hotel. Once beyond the range of the dictograph, however, Campbell advised Blake of his strategy and the two headed for another spot. They found a secluded corner and had their first opportunity for a long talk. "You are in grave danger now, Al," said the intelligence operative. "The Japs have all the information that it would be possible for a man in my position to lay hands on, and they know it. So now you are definitely on the spot."

"You mean that they're going to send me on that Pearl Harbor mission now, and get me along a lonely stretch of road between here and there?"

The intelligence operative nodded. "That's just what they intend to do," he said, "and that's just what we intend to avoid."

Regarding the over-all strategy, Campbell explained that the response of the consular attaché to certain information, as passed on by Blake in his notes to Campbell, had cleared up just about what the Japs knew and didn't know about all phases of the Pacific fleet.

"The result is," the intelligence operative explained, "that we will be able to take certain precautions. We know that when the Japanese attack comes that it will be sudden, and that it will be perpetrated in the midst of diplomatic negotiations that will be carried on in Washington between Japanese representatives and our State Department.

"We know now just about what the Japanese have in mind. All we have to do is be alert twenty-four hours a day." And then the operative made a prophetic remark. "Of course," he said, "it is always possible that there might be a slip-up somewhere. For instance, our information may not be taken as seriously as it should be in certain quarters. That's often so with information of this kind. Certain people doubt it, because a good deal of it is deduction. God help us if any of this is doubted."

Before the intelligence operative and Blake parted for the night, the spurious yeoman cautioned Blake, "I'll be over again sometime tomorrow. Whatever you do, don't leave your room until I get there. When I arrive I hope we will have something worked out for your escape. If by any chance you get instructions to go out to Pearl Harbor before I arrive, stall them off, whatever you do. Play sick if you have to."

Blake put on his act that night. The next morning, about ten, the Japanese consular attaché called at Blake's room. The King of the Robots gave a splendid imitation of a man suffering from a hangover and the jitters. The Japanese was obviously disappointed at Blake's condition.

"I wanted you to start on that Pearl Harbor business this afternoon," he said. "Do you think you'll be able to go?"

Blake looked at the Japanese woefully. "All I want is my bed," he said. "Couldn't we put it off until tomorrow?"

"Yes," said the Japanese, "I suppose so, if we have to. Will you be ready to start tomorrow afternoon at three?"

"I'll be all right by then," said Blake. "I'm sorry this happened. But it's been a great strain, and I had to relax."

The naval operative called at Blake's at seven that night. After a preliminary conversation, during which the two men dwelt on the amount of drinking they had done the night before, the operative handed Blake a note. It read as follows:

Two men in the next room are the ones who are to kill you. That's definite.

Blake wrote a note:

How do you know?

The answer was:

They were followed this morning to a lonely spot not far from Pearl Harbor where you would have to pass to get there. F.B.I. men using glasses saw them examine the spot apparently where they are to hide until you come along.

Blake asked in another note:

How do you propose to get me out of here?

The answer was ready:

In a little while now you will get a cablegram saying that your mother in Illinois is not expected to live. A boat leaves tomorrow afternoon for San Francisco and you are openly to make arrangements to get on. The Japs will figure that you can probably make the trip to Pearl Harbor earlier so that you could do the job there and still catch the boat. But a Clipper leaves at noon and you can just wander into the Clipper office a few minutes before it goes out as a sort of a second thought to get back to the United States as early as possible and just go out on it. But before you go drop a hasty but nice note to the Japanese Consulate, telling them what you did and explaining that you are almost out of your mind through anxiety about your mother and that you will come back.

The fake cablegram announcing his mother's serious illness arrived for Blake not an hour after Campbell returned to the U.S.S. *Pennsylvania*. Blake smiled grimly as he examined the envelope before opening it. The envelope had been opened, perhaps right in the hotel, before being delivered to him. He opened the cable at the desk where the dictograph was planted so that the listeners could hear what he was doing. As he read the spurious message he gave a deep sigh, muttering the words, "My God—poor mother!" And then he began to sob. Blake did some of his best acting to date in the ten minutes that followed his opening of the message.

The Japanese attaché put in another of his unexpected appearances not half an hour afterward. "I just stopped by to see how you were feeling," he said. Blake handed him the cable. "This is too bad," said the Japanese when he read the message that he had no doubt been acquainted with before entering the room. "What do you intend to do, Mr. Blake?"

"When's the next boat out of here?" asked Blake. "I want to be on it. Something tells me I'll never see my mother again, and I'll come back and do that Pearl Harbor business then."

"Your boat doesn't leave until late tomorrow," declared the Japanese. "A chauffeur will be here with a car before noon to take you out on that job. He will have you back in time."

Blake could only wait, hoping to stage the Clipper caper as Campbell's note had advised. But the next morning, when Blake came down to the hotel lobby, he spotted two men of Teutonic appearance watching him and knew they must be the pair from the next room.

They stalked Blake about the hotel grounds and trailed him to the steamship office when he picked up the ticket he didn't intend to use. When Blake came back to the hotel and went upstairs, they did the same.

It was now about half-past eleven, and Blake realized he would have to set forth if he wanted to catch the Clipper. He decided to shake off the Germans between his room and the entrance of the hotel, where he would get a taxi. The two Nazi killers were in the next room, he knew, for he had heard them enter just after he had himself returned. Blake was leaving his baggage. He didn't want it to look as if the Clipper trip had been planned without the knowledge of his Japanese employers. His departure should have the appearance of a sudden impulse. He put on his hat and was just about to open the door and steal silently downstairs, when suddenly there was a faint rapping on the door.

Opening it, he found a smiling Japanese in a chauffeur's livery. The man obviously was much above his station, however, for there was no deference in his manner. He walked into Blake's room without being invited, closed the door behind him, and said, "I'm a little early; we aren't supposed to start until twelve o'clock."

"Suppose," said Blake, "we go down and sit in your car. I need some air." Blake was certain that the Germans in the next room were listening in, and now that the Japanese chauffeur had arrived they would perhaps leave for the death rendezvous so that they could be well settled before Blake came along. The more Blake thought about the early arrival of the chauffeur, the more he became convinced that the timing was part of the plot.

He stalled for a couple of minutes, going into the bathroom to bathe his face in cold water; he wanted to see whether the Germans would leave in advance of him. They did, for Blake heard the door of their room slamming.

It was twenty-five minutes to noon when Blake and the chauffeur left the room and went down to the car. "What about my last-minute instructions?" Blake asked the chauffeur.

"I am not to give you those until we are nearly to Pearl Harbor, where you are to get out of the car and go on foot." Blake realized that there were to be no more instructions, because the point at which he was to leave the car was well beyond the place where the F.B.I. had observed the Germans rehearsing for murder.

"Say," said Blake, "I've just thought of something: the man I work with mentioned something to me night before last about the Pan-American Clipper base. I think we've just got time enough to ride out there." Blake had a certain hypnotic quality in his eyes, and now he called that quality into play for the first time since he had been dealing with the Japanese. He fastened his gaze on the chauffeur, and the chauffeur nodded and said, "Why not?"

Blake could hardly believe it himself when he realized that the Germans were no longer on his trail and that the Japanese chauffeur was driving him to the very spot where he wanted to get in a hurry.

The car reached the Clipper base only two minutes before the departure of the big ship. Blake rushed in and got the reservation that the Navy had made for him—the last space on the plane. He waited until it was almost time for the departure. Then he rushed outside and handed the chauffeur a note. "Give this to the man in the consulate that I have been dealing with," he instructed the chauffeur. "He never did tell me his name, but I guess you know who he is."

Almost mechanically, the chauffeur took the envelope from Blake and put it in his pocket. "What's going on?" he asked.

Blake, still acting like a man who was almost off-balance mentally, sputtered something about an act of God. The Japanese didn't know what that meant. "Somebody cancelled a Clipper reservation," said the King of the Robots, "and I got it. It would never happen like this in a month of Sundays. Why, I didn't even *try* to get a Clipper reservation. Now I can probably see my mother before she dies."

The chauffeur was nonplussed. Emotions of surprise, anger, and disappointment flickered across his face. "But the job you have to do," he said; "what about that?"

Blake answered that the sooner he arrived in the United States the sooner he could return to pick up where he had left off. "I've explained everything to the consular attaché in this letter," he said. "I've also just run into something here"—he jerked his head toward the Clipper base—"that will beat anything I've found out yet. It's perfectly amazing. It will make the other information seem unimportant by comparison." Blake appeared to force a smile of courtesy through his excitement and sorrow. Then he extended his hand to the chauffeur. "Well," he said, "good-bye until we meet again."

All the way across to California on the Clipper, Blake wondered if the nature of his departure had caused the Japanese to become suspicious. It was just before the Clipper arrived in San Francisco that he received a wireless message which set his mind at rest. The coded dispatch stated that the act he had put on at his departure had been most successful. The O.N.I. did not say just how they had found this out, but he did learn that Naval Intelligence operatives had planted a sound-detection apparatus in the hotel room occupied by the two Germans.

When the Clipper was three hours out and the Germans had returned to the hotel, wondering why Blake had never appeared at the scene of the projected murder, Blake's Japanese chauffeur called on them. A conversation had taken place among the three men, in German. One of the O.N.I. operatives listening in understood German well. The German assassins questioned the chauffeur about the events of the day. The Jap told them of Blake's erratic behavior. The Germans, too, had noticed that he had behaved erratically during the hours before his departure, but had never doubted Blake's motives any more than had the chauffeur.

What pleased the Navy listeners-in more than anything else was the conclusion of the conversation between the Germans and the Japanese. "You men can have a nice vacation here," the Japanese told the Germans, "until Blake comes back. Even in his grief he picked up some information at the Clipper base just before he left and is so excited about it—whatever it is—that he will probably hurry back after his mother dies."

Once more Al Blake was received cordially by Mr. Kono and Commander Tachibana when he returned to Hollywood and met them at Kono's apartment on Bronson Street. Not that these men were pleased to see Blake at all, for they weren't. The King of the Robots divined that the two were just pretending.

Blake said he would have to leave immediately for Illinois, but would return to Hollywood, en route back to the Orient, after he had seen his mother. "I don't know what your people must think of me in Honolulu," said Blake to Commander Tachibana, "because of the way I left. But I just wasn't thinking straight, and won't be until I have seen my mother."

Tachibana asked the nature of the information that Blake had picked up at the Clipper base. Blake revealed certain spurious data that the O.N.I. had thought up for him. Mr. Kono and Commander Tachibana looked at each other. "Perhaps," said Tachibana to Kono, "Mr. Blake will be of further great value to us."

Blake pretended to be unable to get plane connections for Illinois until the following morning, so he and Tachibana and Kono made an appointment to meet that night in a Japanese restaurant on San Pedro Street in Los Angeles. The three of them had a fine sukiyaki dinner and there was a considerable amount of talk during the meal about further espionage work that could be done in Hawaii by, as Commander Tachibana put it, "any smart American."

Before, during and after the meal both Kono and Tachibana drank large quantities of saké—the potent Japanese rice wine that Blake had never seen either of them touch before. Tachibana began to grow voluble about negotiations he had opened whereby he could, within the borders of the United States, lay hands on certain naval data which, he said, he felt certain would prove of greater value to Japan than anything yet picked up by any Japanese operative. This was an unusual thing for Tachibana, who was a close-mouthed official, to do. Perhaps subconsciously he felt that he was now safe in relaxing and talking in front of Al Blake, because Blake was as good as a dead man. He was only on a reprieve, so to speak, through the accident of his mother's sudden illness and the cancellation at the last minute of a Clipper reservation. Blake, though still pretending to be griefstricken, nevertheless displayed such enthusiasm about the latest information he had run across in Hawaii that both Mr. Kono and Commander Tachibana no doubt figured that nothing would stop him from going back.

It was late in the evening when Blake, Kono, and Tachibana left the restaurant. The three were walking along a dark part of the street not far from the restaurant, with Blake on the outside, silent, and Tachibana and Kono jabbering away in Japanese. Suddenly they heard Blake exclaim, "Hey! What the hell is this—a hold-up?"

"No," were the next words the two Japanese heard, "this is not a hold-up. You three men are under arrest." Someone had seized Blake and pinned his arms behind him, and two other men had done the same to Kono and Tachibana. Two or three other men hovered nearby in the darkness.

Blake became the spokesman for Kono and Tachibana. "Under arrest for *what?*" he demanded.

"You'll find out soon enough."

Blake, Kono, and Tachibana were led to a waiting automobile. Their captors, after searching them for weapons —and finding one on Blake—shoved them into the car and got in after them. Not long afterwards the three found themselves in the offices of Lieutenant Stanley of the O.N.I

Kono and Tachibana were practically speechless. Blake put on an act of belligerence. He demanded to know what the O.N.I. had on him. He was told that he had been arrested on suspicion of espionage. "Suspicion, hell!" roared Blake. "What have you got on me that's *definite?*"

Lieutenant Stanley, and other O.N.I. officers, were putting on a good show. They "admitted" that they didn't have anything definite on Blake and the two Japanese. Kono and Tachibana smiled at each other.

Nevertheless the three men were held in custody, and the story was released to the newspapers that Al Blake, as well as Mr. Kono and Commander Tachibana had been arrested on espionage charges. The O.N.I. hadn't figured out

yet just how much evidence it would choose to release
when the two Japanese were indicted and brought to trial.
The whole business was ticklish in the extreme, particularly
since the State Department, hoping against hope that peace
with Japan could be preserved, didn't want such a man as
Commander Tachibana "offended." The fact that the King
of the Robots also was arrested would meanwhile serve as a
smoke screen to cover Blake's real role in the dangerous
espionage game.

The O.N.I. had moved against Tachibana more quickly
than they wanted to. It had originally been the plan of the
O.N.I. to leave Tachibana out on the hook as far as the line
would stretch. But the O.N.I. had learned of his connections
in certain high places within the United States and of his
being in possession of the very information that he had referred to during dinner with Blake that night. The investigators had reason to believe that no other Japanese had this
information and that Tachibana was not going to let his
superiors know about it until he himself returned to Japan.
They had information, too, that Tachibana was about to lay
hands on physical amplification of the information he
had and, as a way of getting this physical evidence safely
past customs inspectors, he had arranged with the Japanese
Government to be appointed, prior to his departure for the
Orient, to the diplomatic corps. Thus his baggage would not
be subject to search.

Certainly the O.N.I. had, in Tachibana, a big fish in the
net. The investigators of that organization and the F.B.I.
were convinced that by the arrest of the commander they
had struck a telling blow against Japan. The underground
from Hawaii was to the effect that Japanese officials in Honolulu were unperturbed over Tachibana's arrest, since a
good deal of the information that Blake had dug up on his
second visit was already in their possession. Moreover,
when the Federal officials in Honolulu made no move to arrest Yeoman Campbell, it probably seemed apparent to the
Japanese that the Federal officials hadn't known about

Campbell. All of which would have left undisturbed the
status of information planted on the Japanese through
Blake.

Then something shameful happened. The State Department, instead of coming out and letting the American
people know what was what, hushed up the Kono and Tachibana affair after the first flurry of excitement in the newspapers. The soft pedal was put on the whole thing when
the State Department decided that it could not risk offend-
ing a "friendly" power. And, believe it or not, Commander
Tachibana's punishment was banishment to the Orient!
Mr. Kono was permitted his liberty, and wasn't snared
again until after Pearl Harbor.

Al Blake's true role in the whole affair did not come out
until after Pearl Harbor. The King of the Robots today
can well regard himself as a patriot who has done much
for his country. Had it not been for his intelligent appraisal
of the reactions of the Japanese to the spurious information
handed them, the tragedy of Pearl Harbor, as bad as it was,
would have been considerably worse.

I Escape from the Boers

In 1907, The Hague Convention defined spying:

> *A person can be considered as a spy when, acting clandestinely or on false pretenses, he obtains or endeavors to obtain information in the zone of operations of a belligerent, with the intention of communicating it to the hostile party.*

That was about how the situation stood at the outset of the Boer War in 1899, except that the Boers were considerably rougher. But at the time, the question of definitions went almost unheeded by a debonair newspaper correspondent from London, who was covering the Boer War for the *Morning Post.*

At the age of twenty-five, the correspondent was being paid the highest price in journalistic history, so he wanted to deliver accordingly. Besides, as he admitted later, he was eager for trouble that November day. He found it, soon after he boarded a British armored train heading into enemy territory. Within fifteen miles, the train was partly wrecked by Boer artillery fire and the correspondent—a former army officer—ordered the engineer to haul a load of soldiers across a bridge and come back for more.

Before that could be accomplished, the Boers arrived in force and the war correspondent, captured as a combatant, had achieved some status as a spy. He most certainly was endeavoring to obtain information for communication to the hostile party through the pages of the *Morning Post*.

Significantly, the Boers imprisoned the correspondent with the British officers, which fixed the first count against him. All he needed to be a full-fledged spy was to act clandestinely by effecting an escape and beating his way back to the British lines. That, of course, was exactly what he decided to do, and perhaps not unwisely.

For while he was still a prisoner, the London *Phoenix* had this to say regarding the captured correspondent:

"The Boer general cannot be blamed should be order his execution. A noncombatant has no right to carry arms. In the Franco-Prussian War, all noncombatants who carried arms were promptly executed when they were caught; and we can hardly expect the Boers to be more humane than were the highly civilized French and Germans."

Such was journalism in those days, but fortunately, communications were slow. By the time copies of the *Phoenix* reached the Boers, their bird had flown.

He later admitted he had recognized his dilemma, for he declared:

"I had enough military law to know that a civilian who has taken an active and prominent part in a fight, even if he has not fired a shot himself, is liable himself to be shot at once by drumhead court-martial. None of the armies in the Great War would have wasted ten minutes upon the business."

He knew, for he went through World War I, in which the highly civilized French and Germans proved much less humane than the Boers. He also went through World War II, where everyone seemed even less humane, though humanity itself may have owed its survival to the oversight of the Boers.

For the correspondent who, in 1899, eluded the firing squad that his own countrymen had recommended, was Winston Churchill. Here is the story of his escape in his own words.

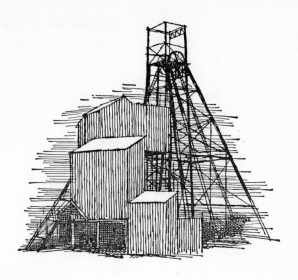

I Escape
from the Boers

WINSTON CHURCHILL

D URING the first three weeks of my captivity, although I was a party to all plans of revolt or escape, I was engaged in arguing with the Boer authorities that they should release me as a press correspondent. They replied that I had forfeited my non-combatant status by the part I had taken in the armored train fight. I contended that I had not fired a shot and had been taken unarmed. This was strictly true. But the Natal newspapers had been captured by the Boers. These contained glowing accounts of my activities, and attributed the escape of the engine and the wounded entirely to me. General Joubert therefore intimated that even if I had not fired a shot myself, I had injured the Boer operations by freeing the engine, and that I must therefore be treated as a prisoner-of-war. As soon as I learned of this decision, in the first week of December, I resolved to escape.

I shall transcribe what I wrote at the time where I cannot improve upon it.

"The State Model Schools stood in the midst of a quadrangle, and were surrounded on two sides by an iron grille and on two by a corrugated-iron fence about ten feet high. These boundaries offered little obstacle to anyone who possessed the activity of youth, but the fact that they were guarded on the inside by sentries, fifty yards apart, armed with rifle and revolver, made them a well-nigh insuperable barrier. No walls are so hard to pierce as living walls.

"After anxious reflection and continual watching, it was discovered by several of the prisoners that when the sentries along the eastern side walked about on their beats they were at certain moments unable to see the top of a few yards of the wall near the small circular lavatory office. The electric lights in the middle of the quadrangle brilliantly lighted the whole place, but the eastern wall was in shadow. The first thing was therefore to pass the two sentries near the office. It was necessary to hit off the exact moment when both their backs should be turned together. After the wall was scaled we should be in the garden of the villa next door. There the plan came to an end. Everything after this was vague and uncertain. How to get out of the garden, how to pass unnoticed through the streets, how to evade the patrols that surrounded the town, and above all how to cover the 280 miles to the Portuguese frontier, were questions which would arise at a later stage.

"Together with Captain Haldane and Lieutenant Brockie I made an abortive attempt, not pushed with any decision, on December 11. There was no difficulty in getting into the circular office. But to climb out of it over the wall was a hazard of the sharpest character. Anyone doing so must at the moment he was on the top of the wall be plainly visible to the sentries fifteen yards away, if they were in the right place and happened to look! Whether the sentries would challenge or fire depended entirely upon their individual dispositions, and no one could tell what they would do. Nevertheless I was determined that nothing should stop my taking the plunge the next day. As the 12th wore away my fears crystallized more and more into desperation. In the evening, after my two friends had made an attempt, but had not found the moment propitious, I strolled across the quadrangle and secreted myself in the circular office. Through an aperture in the metal casing of which it was built I watched the sentries. For some time they remained stolid and obstructive. Then all of a sudden one turned and walked up to his comrade, and they began to talk. Their backs were turned.

"Now or never! I stood on a ledge, seized the top of the wall with my hands, and drew myself up. Twice I let myself down again in sickly hesitation, and then with a third resolve scrambled up and over. My waistcoat got entangled with the ornamental metalwork on the top. I had to pause for an appreciable moment to extricate myself. In this posture I had one parting glimpse of the sentries still talking with their backs turned fifteen yards away. One of them was lighting his cigarette, and I remember the glow on the inside of his hands as a distinct impression which my mind recorded. Then I lowered myself lightly down into the adjoining garden and crouched among the shrubs. I was free! The first step had been taken, and it was irrevocable. It now remained to await the arrival of my comrades. The bushes in the garden gave a good deal of cover, and in the moonlight their shadows fell dark on the ground. I lay here for an hour in great impatience and anxiety. People were continually moving about in the garden, and once a man came and apparently looked straight at me only a few yards away. Where were the others? Why did they not make the attempt?

"Suddenly I heard a voice from within the quadrangle say, quite loud, 'All up.' I crawled back to the wall. Two officers were walking up and down inside, jabbering Latin words, laughing and talking all manner of nonsense—

amid which I caught my name. I risked a cough. One of the officers immediately began to chatter alone. The other said, slowly and clearly, 'They cannot get out. The sentry suspects. It's all up. Can you get back again?' But now all my fears fell from me at once. To go back was impossible. I could not hope to climb the wall unnoticed. There was no helpful ledge on the outside. Fate pointed onwards. Besides, I said to myself, 'Of course, I shall be recaptured, but I will at least have a run for my money.' I said to the officers, 'I shall go on alone.'

"Now I was in the right mood for these undertakings— failure being almost certain, no odds against success affected me. All risks were less than the certainty. The gate which led into the road was only a few yards from another sentry. I said to myself, *'Toujours de l'audace,'* put my hat on my head, strode into the middle of the garden, walked past the windows of the house without any attempt at concealment, and so went through the gate and turned to the left. I passed the sentry at less than five yards. Most of them knew me by sight. Whether he looked at me or not I do not know, for I never turned my head. I restrained with the utmost difficulty an impulse to run. But after walking a hundred yards and hearing no challenge, I knew that the second obstacle had been surmounted. I was at large in Pretoria.

"I walked on leisurely through the night, humming a tune and choosing the middle of the road. The streets were full of burghers, but they paid no attention to me. Gradually I reached the suburbs, and on a little bridge I sat down to reflect and consider. I was in the heart of the enemy's country. I knew no one to whom I could apply for succor. Nearly three hundred miles stretched between me and Delagoa Bay. My escape must be known at dawn. Pursuit would be immediate. Yet all exits were barred. The town was picketed, the country was patrolled, the trains were searched, the line was guarded. I wore a civilian brown flannel suit. I had seventy-five pounds in my pocket and four slabs of chocolate, but the compass and the map which might have guided me, the opium tablets and meat lozenges which should have sustained me, were in my friends' pockets in the State Model Schools. Worst of all, I could not speak a word of Dutch or Kaffir, and how was I to get food or direction?

"But when hope had departed, fear had gone as well. I formed a plan. I would find the Delagoa Bay Railway. Without map or compass, I must follow that in spite of the pickets. I looked at the stars. Orion shone brightly. Scarcely a year before he had guided me when lost in the desert to the banks of the Nile. He had given me water. Now he should lead to freedom. I could not endure the want of either.

"After walking south for half a mile I struck the railroad. Was it the line to Delagoa Bay or the Pietersburg branch? If it were the former, it should run east. But, so far as I could see, this line ran northwards. Still, it might be only winding its way out among the hills. I resolved to follow it. The night was delicious. A cool breeze fanned my face, and a wild feeling of exhilaration took hold of me. At any rate, I was free, if only for an hour. That was something. The fascination of the adventure grew. Unless the stars in their courses fought for me, I could not escape. Where, then, was the need of caution? I marched briskly along the line. Here and there the lights of a picket fire gleamed. Every bridge had its watchers. But I passed them all, making very short *détours* at the dangerous places, and really taking scarcely any precautions. Perhaps that was the reason I succeeded.

"As I walked I extended my plan. I could not march three hundred miles to the frontier. I would board a train in motion and hide under the seats, on the roof, on the couplings—anywhere. I thought of Paul Bultitude's escape from school in *Vice Versa*. I saw myself emerging from under the seat, and bribing or persuading some fat first-class passenger to help me. What train should I take? The first, of course. After walking for two hours I perceived the signal lights of a station. I left the line, and circling round it, hid in the ditch by the track about two hundred yards beyond the platform. I argued that the train would stop at the station and that it would not have got up too much speed by the time it reached me. An hour passed. I began to grow impatient. Suddenly I heard the whistle and the approaching rattle. Then the great yellow headlights of the engine flashed into view. The train waited five minutes at the station, and started again with much noise and steaming. I crouched by the track. I rehearsed the act in my mind. I must wait until the engine had passed, otherwise I should be seen. Then I must make a dash for the carriages.

"The train started slowly, but gathered speed sooner than I had expected. The flaring lights drew swiftly near. The rattle became a roar. The dark mass hung for a second above me. The engine-driver silhouetted against his furnace glow, the black profile of the engine, the clouds of steam rushed past. Then I hurled myself on the trucks, clutched at something, missed, clutched again, missed again, grasped some sort of hand-hold, was swung off my feet—my toes bumping on the line, and with a struggle seated myself on the couplings of the fifth truck from the front of the train. It was a goods train, and the trucks were full of sacks, soft sacks covered with coal dust. They were in fact bags filled with empty coal bags going back to their colliery. I crawled on top and burrowed in among them. In five minutes I was completely buried. The sacks were warm and comfortable. Perhaps the engine-driver had seen me rush up to the train and would give the alarm at the next station; on the other hand, perhaps not. Where was the train going to? Where would it be unloaded? Would it be searched? Was it on the Delagoa Bay line? What should I do in the morning? Ah, never mind that. Sufficient for the night was the luck thereof. Fresh plans for fresh contingencies. I resolved to sleep, nor can I imagine a more pleasing lullaby than the clatter of the train that carries an escaping prisoner at twenty miles an hour away from the enemy's capital.

"How long I slept I do not know, but I woke up suddenly with all feelings of exhilaration gone, and only the consciousness of oppressive difficulties heavy on me. I must leave the train before daybreak, so that I could drink at a pool and find some hiding place while it was still dark. I would not run the risk of being unloaded with the coal bags. Another night I would board another train. I crawled from my cozy hiding place among the sacks and sat again on the couplings. The train was running at a fair speed, but I felt it was time to leave it. I took hold of the iron handle at the back of the truck, pulled strongly with my left hand, and sprang. My feet struck the ground in two gigantic strides, and the next instant I was sprawling in the ditch considerably shaken but unhurt. The train, my faithful ally of the night, hurried on its journey.

"It was still dark. I was in the middle of a wide valley, surrounded by low hills, and carpeted with high grass drenched in dew. I searched for water in the nearest gully, and soon found a clear pool. I was very thirsty, but long after I had quenched my thirst I continued to drink, that I might have sufficient for the whole day.

"Presently the dawn began to break, and the sky to the east grew yellow and red, slashed across with heavy black clouds. I saw with relief that the railway ran steadily towards the sunrise. I had taken the right line, after all.

"Having drunk my fill, I set out for the hills, among which I hoped to find some hiding place, and as it became broad daylight I entered a small grove of trees which grew on the side of a deep ravine. Here I resolved to wait till dusk. I had one consolation: no one in the world knew where I was—I did not know myself. It was now four o'clock. Fourteen hours lay between me and the night. My impatience to proceed while I was still strong doubled their length. At first it was terribly cold, but by degrees the sun gained power, and by ten o'clock the heat was oppressive. My sole companion was a gigantic vulture, who manifested an extravagant interest in my condition, and made hideous and ominous gurglings from time to time.

From my lofty position I commanded a view of the whole valley. A little tin-roofed town lay three miles to the westward. Scattered farmsteads, each with a clump of trees, relieved the monotony of the undulating ground. At the foot of the hill stood a Kaffir *kraal,* and the figures of its inhabitants dotted the patches of cultivation or surrounded the droves of goats and cows which fed on the pasture. . . . During the day I ate one slab of chocolate, which, with the heat, produced a violent thirst. The pool was hardly half a mile away, but I dared not leave the shelter of the little wood, for I could see the figures of white men riding or walking occasionally across the valley, and once a Boer came and fired two shots at birds close to my hiding place. But no one discovered me.

"The elation and the excitement of the previous night had burnt away, and a chilling reaction followed. I was very hungry, for I had had no dinner before starting, and chocolate, though it sustains, does not satisfy. I had scarcely slept, but yet my heart beat so fiercely and I was so nervous and perplexed about the future that I could not rest. I thought of all the chances that lay against me; I dreaded and detested more than words can express the prospect of being caught and dragged back to Pretoria. I found no comfort in any of the philosophical ideas which some men parade in their hours of ease and strength and safety. They seemed only fair weather friends. I realized with awful force that no exercise of my own feeble wit and strength could save me from my enemies, and that without the assistance of that High Power which interferes in the eternal sequence of causes and effects more often than we are always prone to admit, I could never succeed. I prayed long and earnestly for help and guidance. My prayer, as it seems to me, was swiftly and wonderfully answered."

I wrote these lines many years ago while the impression of the adventure was strong upon me. Then I could tell no more. To have done so would have compromised the liberty and perhaps the lives of those who had helped me. For many years these reasons have disappeared. The time has come when I can relate the events which followed, and which changed my nearly hopeless position into one of superior advantage.

During the day I had watched the railway with attention. I saw two or three trains pass along it each way. I argued that the same number would pass at night. I resolved to board one of these. I thought I could improve on my procedure of the previous evening. I had observed how slowly the trains, particularly long goods-trains, climbed some of the steep gradients. Sometimes they were hardly going at a foot's pace. It would probably be easy to choose a point where the line was not only on an upgrade but also on a curve. Thus I could board some truck on the convex side of the train when both the engine and the guard's van were bent away, and when consequently neither the engine-driver nor the guard would see me. This plan seemed to me in every respect sound. I saw myself leaving the train again before dawn, having been carried forward another sixty or seventy miles during the night. That would be scarcely one hundred and fifty miles from the frontier. And why should not the process be repeated? Where was the flaw? I could not see it. With three long bounds on three successive nights I could be in Portuguese territory. Meanwhile I still had two or three slabs of chocolate and a pocketful of crumbled biscuit—enough, that is to say, to keep body and soul together at a pinch without running the awful risk of recapture entailed by accosting a single human being. In this mood I watched with increasing impatience the arrival of darkness.

The long day reached its close at last. The western clouds flushed into fire; the shadows of the hills stretched out across the valley; a ponderous Boer wagon with its long team crawled slowly along the track towards the township; the Kaffirs collected their herds and drew them round their *kraal;* the daylight died, and soon it was quite dark. Then, and not until then, I set forth. I hurried to the railway line, scrambling along through the boulders and high grass and pausing on my way to drink at a stream of sweet cold water. I made my way to the place where I had seen the trains crawling so slowly up the slope, and soon found a point where the curve of the track fulfilled all the conditions of my plan. Here, behind a little bush, I sat down and waited hopefully. An hour passed; two hours passed; three hours—and yet no train. Six hours had now elapsed since the last, whose time I had carefully noted, had gone by. Surely one was due. Another hour slipped away. Still no train! My plan began to crumble and my hopes to ooze out of me. After all, was it not quite possible that no trains ran on this part of the line during the dark hours? This was in fact the case, and I might well have continued to wait in vain till daylight. However, between twelve and one in the morning I lost patience and started along the track, resolved to cover at any rate ten or fifteen miles of my journey. I did not make much progress. Every bridge was guarded by armed men; every few miles were huts. At intervals there were stations with tin-roofed villages clustering around them. All the veldt was bathed in the bright rays of the full moon, and to avoid these dangerous places I had to make wide circuits and even to creep along the ground. Leaving the railroad I fell into bogs and swamps, brushed through high grass dripping with dew, and waded across the streams over which the bridges carried the railway. I was soon drenched to the waist. I had been able to take very little exercise during my month's imprisonment, and I was quickly tired with walking and with want of food and sleep. Presently I approached a station. It was a mere platform in the veldt, with two or three buildings and huts around it. But laid up on the sidings, obviously for the night, were three long goods-trains. Evidently the flow of traffic over the railway was uneven. These three trains, motionless in the moonlight, confirmed my fears that traffic was not maintained by night on this part of the line. Where, then, was my plan which in the afternoon had looked so fine and sure?

It now occurred to me that I might board one of these stationary trains immediately, and hiding amid its freight be carried forward during the next day—and night too if all were well. On the other hand, where were they going to? Where would they stop? Where would they be unloaded? Once I entered a wagon my lot would be cast. I might find myself ignominiously unloaded and recaptured at Witbank or Middleburg, or at any station in the long two hundred miles which separated me from the frontier. It was necessary at all costs before taking such a step to find out where these trains were going. To do this I must penetrate the station, examine the labels on the trucks or on the merchandise, and see if I could extract any certain guidance from them. I crept up to the platform and got between two of the long trains on the siding. I was proceeding to examine the markings on the trucks when loud voices rapidly approaching on the outside of the trains filled me with fear. Several Kaffirs were laughing and shouting in their unmodulated tones, and I heard, as I thought, a European voice arguing or ordering. At any rate, it was enough for me. I retreated between the two trains to the extreme end of the siding, and slipped stealthily but rapidly into the grass of the illimitable plain.

There was nothing for it but to plod on—but in an increasingly purposeless and hopeless manner. I felt very miserable when I looked around and saw here and there the lights of houses and thought of the warmth and comfort within them, but knew that they meant only danger to me. Far off on the moonlit horizon there presently began to shine the row of six or eight big lights which marked either Witbank or Middleburg station. Out in the darkness to my left gleamed two or three fires. I was sure they were not the lights of houses, but how far off they were or what they were I could not be certain. The idea formed in my mind that they were the fires of a Kaffir *kraal*. Then I began to think that the best use I could make of my remaining strength would be to go to these Kaffirs. I had heard that they hated the Boers and were friendly to the British. At any rate, they would probably not arrest me. They might give me food and a dry corner to sleep in. Although I could not speak a word of their language, yet I thought perhaps they might understand the value of a British bank note. They might even be induced to help me. A guide, a pony— but, above all, rest, warmth, and food—such were the promptings which dominated my mind. So I set out towards the fires.

I must have walked a mile or so in this resolve before a realisation of its weakness and imprudence took possession of me. Then I turned back again to the railway line and retraced my steps perhaps half the distance. Then I stopped and sat down, completely baffled, destitute of any idea what to do or where to turn. Suddenly without the slightest reason all my doubts disappeared. It was certainly by no process of logic that they were dispelled. I just felt quite clear that I would go to the Kaffir *kraal*. I had sometimes in former years held a "Planchette" pencil and written while others had touched my wrist or hand. I acted in exactly the same unconscious or subconscious manner now.

I walked on rapidly towards the fires, which I had in the first instance thought were not more than a couple of miles from the railway line. I soon found they were much farther away than that. After about an hour or an hour and a half they still seemed almost as far off as ever. But I persevered, and presently between two and three o'clock in the morning I perceived that they were not the fires of a Kaffir *kraal*. The angular outline of buildings began to draw out against them, and soon I saw that I was approaching a group of houses around the mouth of a coal mine. The wheel which worked the winding gear was plainly visible, and I could see that the fires which had led me so far were from the furnaces of the engines. Hard by, surrounded by one or two slighter structures, stood a small but substantial stone house two stories high.

I halted in the wilderness to survey this scene and to revolve my action. It was still possible to turn back. But in that direction I saw nothing but the prospect of further futile wanderings terminated by hunger, fever, discovery, or surrender. On the other hand, here in front was a chance. I had heard it said before I escaped that in the mining district of Witbank and Middleburg there were a certain number of English residents who had been suffered to remain in the country in order to keep the mines working. Had I been led to one of these? What did this house which frowned dark and inscrutable upon me contain? A Briton or a Boer; a friend or a foe? Nor did this exhaust the possibilities. I had my seventy-five pounds in English notes in my pocket. If I revealed my identity, I thought that I could give reasonable assurance of a thousand. I might find some indifferent neutral-minded person who out of good nature or for a large sum of money would aid me in my bitter and desperate need. Certainly I would try to make what bargain I could now—now while I still had the strength to plead my cause and perhaps to extricate myself if the results were adverse. Still the odds were heavy against me, and it was with faltering and reluctant steps that I walked out of the shimmering gloom of the veldt into the light of the furnace fires, advanced towards the silent house, and struck with my fist upon the door.

There was a pause. Then I knocked again. And almost immediately a light sprang up above and an upper window opened.

"Wer ist da?" cried a man's voice.

I felt the shock of disappointment and consternation to my fingers.

"I want help; I have had an accident," I replied.

Some muttering followed. Then I heard steps descending the stairs, the bolt of the door was drawn, the lock was turned. It was opened abruptly, and in the darkness of the passage a tall man hastily attired, with a pale face and dark mustache, stood before me.

"What do you want?" he said, this time in English.

I had now to think of something to say. I wanted above all to get into parley with this man, to get matters in such a state that instead of raising an alarm and summoning others he would discuss things quietly.

"I am a burgher," I began. "I have had an accident. I was going to join my commando at Komati Poort. I have fallen off the train. We were skylarking. I have been unconscious for hours. I think I have dislocated my shoulder."

It is astonishing how one thinks of these things. This story leapt out as if I had learned it by heart. Yet I had not the slightest idea what I was going to say or what the next sentence would be.

The stranger regarded me intently, and after some hesitation said at length, "Well, come in." He retreated a little into the darkness of the passage, threw open a door on one side of it, and pointed with his left hand into a dark room. I walked past him and entered, wondering if it was to be my prison. He followed, struck a light, lit a lamp, and set it on the table at the far side of which I stood. I was in a small room, evidently a dining room and office in one. I noticed besides the large table, a roll desk, two or three chairs, and one of those machines for making soda water, consisting of two glass globes set one above the other and encased in thin wire netting. On his end of the table my host had laid a revolver, which he had hitherto presumably been holding in his right hand.

"I think I'd like to know a little more about this railway accident of yours," he said, after a considerable pause.

"I think," I replied, "I had better tell you the truth."

"I think you had," he said slowly.

So I took the plunge and threw all I had upon the board.

"I am Winston Churchill, war correspondent of the *Morning Post*. I escaped last night from Pretoria. I am making my way to the frontier." (Making my way!) "I have plenty of money. Will you help me?"

There was another long pause. My companion rose from the table slowly and locked the door. After this act, which struck me as unpromising, and was certainly ambiguous, he advanced upon me and suddenly held out his hand.

"Thank God you have come here! It is the only house for twenty miles where you would not have been handed over. But we are all British here, and we will see you through."

It is easier to recall across the gulf of years the spasm of relief which swept over me, than it is to describe it. A moment before I had thought myself trapped; and now friends, food, resources, aid were all at my disposal. I felt like a drowning man pulled out of the water and informed he has won the Derby!

My host now introduced himself as Mr. John Howard, manager of the Transvaal Collieries. He had become a naturalised burgher of the Transvaal some years before the war. But out of consideration for his British race and some inducements which he had offered to the local Field Cornet, he had not been called up to fight against the British. Instead he had been allowed to remain with one or two others on the mine, keeping it pumped out and in good order until coal-cutting could be resumed. He had with him at the mine-head, besides his secretary, who was British, an engine-man from Lancashire and two Scottish miners. All these four were British subjects and had been allowed to remain only upon giving their parole to observe strict neutrality. He himself as burgher of the Transvaal Republic would be guilty of treason in harboring me, and liable to be shot if caught at the time or found out later on.

"Never mind," he said, "we will fix it up somehow." And added, "The Field Cornet was round here this afternoon asking about you. They have got the hue and cry out all along the line and all over the district."

I said that I did not wish to compromise him.

Let him give me food, a pistol, a guide, and if possible a pony, and I would make my own way to the sea, marching by night across country far away from the railway line or any habitation.

He would not hear of it. He would fix up something. But

he enjoined the utmost caution. Spies were everywhere. He had two Dutch servant-maids actually sleeping in the house. There were many Kaffirs employed about the mine premises and on the pumping machinery of the mine. Surveying these dangers he became very thoughtful.

Then: "But you are famishing."

I did not contradict him. In a moment he had bustled off into the kitchen, telling me meanwhile to help myself from a whisky bottle and the soda-water machine which I have already mentioned. He returned after an interval with the best part of a cold leg of mutton and various other delectable commodities, and, leaving me to do full justice to these, quitted the room and let himself out of the house by a back door.

Nearly an hour passed before Mr. Howard returned. In this period my physical well-being had been brought into harmony with the improvement in my prospects. I felt confident of success and equal to anything.

"It's all right," said Mr. Howard. "I have seen the men, and they are all for it. We must put you down the pit tonight, and there you will have to stay till we can see how to get you out of the country. One difficulty," he said, "will be the *skoff* (food). The Dutch girl sees every mouthful I eat. The cook will want to know what has happened to her leg of mutton. I shall have to think it all out during the night. You must get down the pit at once. We'll make you comfortable enough."

Accordingly, just as the dawn was breaking, I followed my host across a little yard into the enclosure in which stood the winding-wheel of the mine. Here a stout man, introduced as Mr. Dewsnap, of Oldham, locked my hand in a grip of crushing vigor.

"They'll all vote for you next time," he whispered.

A door was opened and I entered the cage. Down we shot into the bowels of the earth. At the bottom of the mine were the two Scottish miners with lanterns and a big bundle which afterwards proved to be a mattress and

blankets. We walked for some time through the pitchy laby-
rinth, with frequent turns, twists, and alterations of level,
and finally stopped in a sort of chamber where the air was
cool and fresh. Here my guide set down his bundle, and Mr.
Howard handed me a couple of candles, a bottle of whisky,
and a box of cigars.

"There's no difficulty about these," he said. "I keep them
under lock and key. Now we must plan how to feed you tomorrow."

"Don't you move from here, whatever happens," was
the parting injunction. "There will be Kaffirs about the
mine after daylight, but we shall be on the lookout that none
of them wanders this way. None of them has seen anything so far."

My four friends trooped off with their lanterns, and I
was left alone. Viewed from the velvety darkness of the pit,
life seemed bathed in rosy light. After the perplexity and
even despair through which I had passed I counted upon
freedom as certain. Instead of a humiliating recapture
and long months of monotonous imprisonment, probably
in the common jail, I saw myself once more rejoining the
Army with a real exploit to my credit, and in that full enjoyment of freedom and keen pursuit of adventure dear to
the heart of youth. In this comfortable mood, and speeded
by intense fatigue, I soon slept the sleep of the weary—but
of the triumphant.

The Dark Invader

THE fortunes of war are especially fickle in espionage. To Franz von Rintelen, a captain in the German Navy of World War I, came orders that were not entirely to his liking. He was to proceed to the United States under an assumed name and there use his naval training to impede, sabotage, or destroy all efforts to supply munitions to the Allied Nations.

That was in March, 1915, two years before America entered the war, so Von Rintelen had considerable scope. He secretly delivered a new code to members of the German Embassy to supplant any that the Allies might have already broken. Then he went about his hidden mission which soon assumed fantastic proportions.

Using the interned German liner, the *Friedrich der Grosse* as headquarters, Von Rintelen became a "dark invader" who supervised the manufacture of time bombs that were planted in the cargoes of munitions ships. To facilitate this, he actually sold war supplies to Russian buyers under the name of E. V. Gibbons, Ltd., a fictitious but presumably reputable British firm. He even founded a dockworker's union called Labor's National Peace Council, to foment strikes and delay the loading of Allied cargoes. Operating as head of the Mexico Northwestern Railway, another nonexistent company, Von Rintelen conspired with a former Mexican president, Victoriano Huerta, to stir up a revolt that could have caused war between Mexico and the United States.

From the start, Von Rintelen was aided by capable operatives who were already in New York, awaiting only the arrival of someone who could mastermind their clandestine activities. The compact group included Max Weiser, who acted as a "front" for some of Von Rintelen's well faked business ventures and also enlisted the services of Irishmen who were antagonistic toward England and therefore sympathetic to the German cause.

There was also a lawyer known as Mr. Boniface, who was frequently called in as a trouble-shooter and who never failed to supply the needed answer. In striking contrast was Dr. Scheele, the eccentric chemist, who supplied Von Rintelen with "cigars" in the form of incendiary time bombs, which really were shaped like cigars.

Added to such helpers was a hard-core contingent consisting of the captains of interned German liners. They were waiting for the day when they could burst loose all over the high seas as sitting ducks for waiting British cruisers, a day which fortunately for them—the German captains, not the British cruisers—never came.

How all these elements figured, with their purposes and cross-purposes, is well covered in the following excerpt from Von Rintelen's book, *The Dark Invader*. The narrative begins soon after his arrival in New York. . . .

The Dark Invader

FRANZ VON RINTELEN

M Y assistants came in the evenings, and we discussed in my office what we should do next. The Irish had already thought out a plan. They knew their countrymen who worked in the docks as stevedores and lightermen and told me that these people were willing to plant our "cigars" on British munition transports. They had even chosen a ship, the *Phoebus,* which was to sail in a few days, and whose hold was packed with shells. I opened the drawer of my desk which contained the case of detonators, and it was soon emptied. Next morning the dockers who were in the plot carried their barrels, cases, and sacks on board the *Phoebus,* and as soon as they had assured themselves that they were unobserved, they bent down swiftly in a dark corner of the hold and hid one of our detonators among the cargo. When the *Phoebus* left for Archangel, with a cargo of high explosive shells on

129

board, it carried two of these destructive articles in each of
three holds.

I walked unobtrusively past the steamer while my men
were at work, looked down the open hatchways through
which the cases of shells were being lowered and saw the
British agents who were standing guard on deck, carbines
slung across their arms ready to prevent anything suspicious
from approaching their valuable cargoes. That evening my
assistants came to the office. They were in good humor, and
reported that the *Phoebus* was to sail on the next day, and
that they had placed detonators in some other ships too,
which were to leave harbor a few days later. We had now
used up all our supply, and Dr. Scheele was instructed to prepare some more.

We sat in our office and waited for the first success. We
had subscribed to the *Shipping News,* which printed the
daily reports of Lloyd's in London concerning everything
to do with shipping and shipping insurance. We had cal-
culated the date on which the "accident" was to take place,
but a few days passed and there was still nothing about the
Phoebus in the paper. Suddenly we saw:

> *"Accidents.*   S.S. *Phoebus* from New York—destina-
> tion Archangel—caught fire at sea. Brought into port of
> Liverpool by H.M.S. *Ajax."*

This was our first success, and everything had happened
just as we had planned. Our dockers had of course only put
the detonators in the holds which contained no munitions,
for we had no intention of blowing up the ship from neutral
territory. If we had wished to do so we could have used different means, but we achieved our purpose without the cost
of human life. When the ship caught fire on the open sea the
captain naturally had the munition hold flooded to eliminate
the most serious danger. None of the ships reached its port
of destination, and most of them sank after the crew had

been taken off by other vessels. In every case the explosives
were flooded and rendered useless.

On my visits to the offices of the brokers who dealt in explosives I had seen a large number of British, French, and
Russian agents. At one of the large New York banks, which
carried the account of "E. V. Gibbons Inc.," there was a
manager with whom I soon became rather friendly, but who
only knew that I was one of the partners of our firm and
thought I was an Englishman. He had no idea of my real
identity. I put in an occasional appearance at the Produce
Exchange, in order to keep in touch with what was happening, and sometimes I was addressed by various people as Mr.
Gibbons. As a matter of fact, there really was a Mr. Gibbons, whose name had been entered in a perfectly legal manner in the Commercial Register when we founded our firm,
but who never appeared in his own office, was never seen,
and whom nobody knew. These circumstances gave me an
idea, which occurred to me when I was one day asked by my
bank why I did not try to procure one of the contracts which
the Allies were negotiating with American armament firms.
These contracts were not for munitions alone, but also for
military equipment of all kinds, from shoe leather to mules.
With one of these contracts in one's pocket one could go to
any bank and obtain an advance on it. They were the most
desirable documents that an American businessman could
possess. I thought over a plan during a sleepless night and
set to work next morning with the full realization that the
consequences might be strange and fateful. I went to see a
family that I knew very well—German-Americans, whose
sympathies were so wholly with Germany that they were
ready to do anything to help the Fatherland and injure its
opponents. I required the help of the lady of the house who
had spent a long time in Paris and was particularly well acquainted with Colonel Count Ignatieff, the Russian Military
Attaché in that capital.

Count Ignatieff played an important role in the European

War game. He was clever and energetic, and his post gave
him influence and power. It was clear that he could be of
great use to me. He was especially fond of the material pleas-
ures of life and was celebrated far and wide as a connoisseur
of claret. At my request the lady wrote him a letter conveying the information that an American merchant, Mr. Gibbons, desired to import claret into America, and she requested the Count to help him in the matter with his valuable
advice.

A reply came by night letter to the effect that the Count
would be delighted to be of service to Mr. Gibbons. My firm
now came into action. Weiser wrote the most convincing letters, was unsparing in telegrams, and we were eventually in
possession of a large consignment of claret. Count Ignatieff
had sponsored the transaction. We were a sound firm, and
we cabled the purchase price to France. Weiser was quite
excited when the deal was concluded, for I told him that we
should undoubtedly be able to dispose of the wine. I did not
see him for two days after this, when he turned up again
completely exhausted but happy. The wine was sold before
he was back in New York.

We now wrote another letter to the Count, suggesting that
it would be advantageous for both parties if the Russian
Army would employ our old-established and extremely well-
capitalized firm for their purchases in America. We were in
a position to supply everything that the Russian Army might
need, and we inquired whether it would be possible for us to
obtain a large contract for military equipment.

Ignatieff replied at once. He wrote that of course there
was nothing to stop us from receiving large army contracts,
but that we should first of all get in touch with the Russian
agents in New York, who were there for the purpose of negotiating with American firms. He gave us full permission to
use his name for reference, and made things easy for us by
telling us to whom to go.

On my voyage over in the *Kristianiafjord* I had followed
Ulysses' example and refused to stop my ears to the constant

and compromising chatter of my fellow passengers—many of whom were Russian emissaries of importance, hot on the trail of American munitions. I little thought how and where I was to meet with them again.

I set out, and soon found one of them who was living in a New York hotel, and who had come over to arrange for the supply of war material. I was Mr. Gibbons, and acted in a way that persuaded him that I was a hundred percent American citizen. But the Russian was reserved. He had already given all the contracts that were available, and he invited me to return in six weeks. He then stood up to show me out, but I sat more comfortably in my chair and suggested that what he had just told me would sadden a very good friend of mine. The Russian only listened to me with half an ear and said that he was in a hurry. We were sitting in the lobby of the hotel, and in order to show me that the interview was really at an end he summoned a page to fetch him his hat and coat. I thereupon drew out Count Ignatieff's letter, played with it a moment, and asked him whether he knew his distinguished colleague in Paris, the Military Attaché Count Ignatieff. If so, I should be glad if he would give him my kind regards when he happened to be passing through Paris, and explain to him why he had not been able to help me. I was sure that the Attaché would be interested. The agent looked at me in astonishment, and when I saw that I had made an impression I handed him Count Ignatieff's letter. He read it and was a changed man. It was clear that Ignatieff was too influential a person in the Russian Army for an ordinary captain of infantry, who had been sent to New York on account of his linguistic knowledge, to fall out with. He immediately begged my pardon, grew rather embarrassed, and we went up to his room. After some desultory talk I made things easy for him, and he confessed that he had, as a matter of fact, not yet placed all his contracts for the immediate future, and he declared his willingness to hand all those that remained to E. V. Gibbons Inc.

I told him that I should shortly be going to Paris and

that I would not fail to inform Count Ignatieff of the great courtesy and good favor that my companion had shown me. We went to a lawyer and put through an amazing deal. I received contracts to supply saddles, tinned meat, bridles, mules, horses, field kitchens, boots, shoes, underwear, gloves, and small arms ammunition. I signed a dozen contracts, and the Russian called on his Military Attaché, after he had asked me, as a matter of precaution, to let him have Count Ignatieff's letter. The contracts arrived by post on the following day. They were signed by the Imperial Russian Embassy at Washington, and were worth good money. For anyone else they would have meant great profits, but the Russians would learn in good time with whom they had placed their contracts.

I left the papers in a drawer for some time, and then sent for Boniface to discuss with him the possibilities. He knew all the subterfuges for evading the American commercial laws, and declared at once that nothing could happen to us.

I took the contracts obtrusively and ostentatiously to my bank, so much so that all the inquiry bureaus in New York entered in their registers the fact that the firm of E. V. Gibbons Inc. was carrying out large orders for the Allied armies. This was a distinct help. I obtained advances on my contracts for a magnificent amount, and deposited the money, about three million dollars, in a secret account at another bank.

I now awaited events. The goods were to be delivered in forty-five days, but a fortnight after the signing of the contracts the Russian agents telephoned to ask whether we could possibly deliver sooner. They were prepared to pay a bonus. I was sorry, but it was out of the question. Two Russians came to see me, and I learned that the man with whom I had conducted the original negotiations had gone to Archangel. They told me that it was of the utmost importance to fulfil the contracts at the earliest moment, and showed me telegrams to the effect that things were getting serious for the

Russian troops, who were beginning to suffer a shortage of everything. I was promised a large sum for each day I could save.

I thought deeply. If I persisted in my refusal they might do something that would upset my scheme. They might hurriedly buy up everything they needed and send it across. So I compromised.

"What are the most important items?"

The most important items were tinned provisions and infantry ammunition. I promised to give them an answer the same evening.

I had a hasty conference with Weiser and Boniface. Weiser shot out of the office, rang me up an hour later, and reported that he had succeeded in procuring the necessary tinned stuffs. He had purchased them in three different quarters, and I at once telephoned to the Russians that the provisions could be put on board as soon as they wished. Meanwhile I had myself looked round for ammunition, and eventually obtained as much as I wanted from brokers of all sorts.

The Russians were happy to hear my news. They came at once to my office and told me they had chartered a steamer so that the shipment could begin on the next day. I summoned my captains, and although I did not tell them exactly what I had done, I gave them to understand that we had been able to arrange for Allied supplies to pass through our hands, and that we should be handling the cases of ammunition and tinned foods on the way from the brokers to the ship. They knew what they had to do.

Next day Weiser rented a large store shed at the docks through which we sent the goods. I wanted to make quite sure, for I had a dreadful fear that my plan might miscarry, and I insisted on no less than thirty detonators being placed on the ship. It was quite simple, for we only had to put them in the provision cases. They were laid among wood shavings to ensure their effect.

The boat carried nothing but our supplies. I was given my

check at the dock, together with a second one to cover the
bonus, which was very high, for the days that had been
saved.

I waited for four days in a state of fever. The Russians
telephoned every day in their anxiety to obtain the horses
and mules that I had promised them. I had no intention,
however, of buying these. I sat in my office with nerves on
edge, until at last the *Shipping News* announced that the
steamer had caught fire on the high seas, flames having
broken out simultaneously from every corner of the vessel;
that the crew had taken to the boats, and the ship had
foundered. The crew had been rescued by an American
steamer.

Half an hour later the Russians were wringing their hands
in my office. I pretended to be overwhelmed and promised
to help them. By the evening I had collected enough tinned
provisions and infantry ammunition for two ships, and we
carried out the same operation that had been so effective
with the first consignment. This time I engaged numerous
detectives from a reliable agency, and distributed them about
the ships to see that nobody should sneak on board without
authority. The cases were loaded without incident. I again
snatched up the *Shipping News* every morning, and again
the ships took fire on the high seas. I had promised to supply
twenty-one shiploads in all, and it never occurred to the
Russians that the conflagrations had been engineered by the
contractor, since in any case ships carrying other people's
goods often came to the same end.

The day arrived when I had to deliver the remainder of
the supplies. I had been told by my captains some time
before that another ship or two could be loaded with war
materials for the Allies, and that it was only necessary to
make certain it could be done from the Black Tom Pier.
I should continue to arrange for the cases to be stored in
barges, after they had been taken from the trains, and our
barges would then come alongside the steamer. I knew that
it was safe to follow the advice of the experienced old cap-

tains. By the appointed day I had again purchased enough materials for one shipload, and I went with the Russians to the dock, showed them the goods trains, handed over their contents, and demanded my check. The agents, however, had bought the goods "f.o.b." and declined to pay until they were actually in the holds.

I shrugged my shoulders and pointed out that it was illegal to convey explosives through the harbor. For each case it was necessary to conduct long negotiations with the New York police before a license was received; but the grant of this license was always bound up with so much red tape that in practice hardly a single consignment of munitions which passed through the harbor in barges was reported beforehand, or carried the regulation black flag to advertise its dangerous cargo. The Russians raged inwardly, but I stuck firmly to my refusal, and after some exchange of words, during which the Russians nearly had apoplexy, I received my check and gave orders for the loading to begin. It took place next day under remarkable circumstances. The barges were packed to capacity and two little tugs came to tow them alongside the two steamers which were to take the cases on board. They did not reach the steamers, however, for one barge after another slowly but steadily heeled over, and finally they all lay peacefully together at the bottom of New York Harbor. The tugs had quickly hove to when the barges began to go down, and took on board the few men who had been on them.

Nobody was particularly excited about the disaster; the owners of the barges were not in a position to make capital out of it, for they had acted in defiance of the police regulations, and only the Russian agents appeared next morning with pale faces in my office. It had still not occurred to them that our firm had some slight connection with their misfortunes, but they anxiously demanded the immediate delivery of the rest of the supplies that they had bought from me. I spoke of *force majeure* and strikes, of transport difficulties, and everything else I could think of. I finally told them straight out that I had no intention of delivering the goods. The Russian officers were struck speechless. I shrugged my shoulders; they grew wild, I remained calm. They began to abuse me, so I took my hat and left them.

They sent their lawyers, and Boniface spoke to them. Meanwhile I went to the bank to pay back my advances; and the bonuses I had earned on the three sunken steamers sufficed to pay the interest. I went home with the conviction that I had done a good job. By the time the Russians were ready to take legal proceedings the firm of E. V. Gibbons Inc. no longer existed.

After this success I extended my organization. Dr. Scheele worked day and night to manufacture detonators, and results continued to be gratifying. The number of accidents at sea reported in Lloyd's *Shipping List* increased, and *The New York Times* published on its front page an item of news which cheered us. On July 5th the Russian Minister Prince Miliukov had delivered a speech in the Duma regretting that the delay in the transport of munitions from America was becoming more and more serious, and that it would be necessary to take firm steps to discover the cause and trap the miscreants who were responsible for it.

We were greatly encouraged by this, for it showed us that we were successfully paralyzing the transport of munitions to Russia and helping our troops on the battlefields; so we continued to place bomb after bomb. I founded "branches" in Boston, Philadelphia, Baltimore, and, gradually, in the southern ports of the United States. It was difficult to get our detonators to these towns, for they had to be hidden in the luggage of our confidential agents who traveled regularly round those ports. My most fanatical helpers in this way were the Irish. They swarmed about the various ports with detonators in their pockets and lost no opportunity of having a smack at an English ship. They still did not know who I was, for they had been told that I was connected with Irish Home Rule organizations. I soon, however, had to refrain from employing them, for in their blind hatred of England they had begun to use their bombs in a way we had not intended. They were throwing caution to the winds, and when I turned up at my office one morning Max Weiser came rushing to meet me on the stairs.

"Captain," he whispered in agitation, "something absolutely idiotic has happened. One of our Irishmen has just boasted to me that he has put two of our 'cigars' into the mail room of the *Ancona*."

The *Ancona!* She was a large English mail boat, carrying passengers, and I was thunderstruck at the news. If a fire broke out in the mail room of this steamer, the passengers would be in the greatest danger, and a conflagration on such a well-known boat would attract the attention of the whole world. It might be guessed that there was a connection between this and the "accidents" on the munition transports, and if the New York police got on to our track our work would be rendered vastly more difficult, or even impossible. In any case, it was a senseless thing, for there were passengers on board the *Ancona*, but no shells.

Weiser left me standing on the steps and dashed out. Luckily the Irishman had given him details, and we knew that the "cigars" were in a cardboard box, made up as a postal package. Weiser knew the address that was on it, and after a long talk with the postal official on the *Ancona* and the exchange of some dollar bills of large denomination, he returned, out of breath but happy, with the dangerous parcel in his pocket.

I received cipher messages from all ports with the names of the ships in which my men were putting bombs, and I carefully examined the *Shipping News* to see what happened to them. In many cases a fire broke out and the munitions were rendered useless. Sometimes, however, the fire must have been rapidly extinguished, for about half the ships we were interested in came off unscathed, or else the bombs must have failed. I sent for Dr. Scheele to see if it might not be possible to perfect his invention, though I was in any case convinced that I must find other methods too; but I could not think of any, and when the chemist called we discussed his "cigars" and various other matters. We had exhausted our subjects of conversation, but he still sat tight, and I suddenly had an uneasy feeling that he had come to the office with sinister intentions. I looked past him through the window, where darkness was beginning to fall, when all at once he stood beside me at my desk and snarled:

"If I don't have ten thousand dollars this evening I am going straight to the police."

I continued to gaze through the window. I had long realized that an attempt at blackmail was bound to come, since we had been compelled to initiate a number of shady individuals into our plans, but I was firmly resolved not to yield to any such threats, for if I did so I should be finished. I soon pulled my wits together and came to the conclusion that I could not take the immediate risk of telling the man to go to the devil. He still stood tensely at my side, so I turned to him and said:

"Yes, of course I'll give you the money. Will a check be all right?"

I heard his breath hiss through his teeth with relief as he replied:

"Yes, Captain, a check will suit me."

"But the banks are closed."

"They will be open early tomorrow morning."

I gave him the check and he was perfectly content. I could see in his eyes that he believed he had achieved his purpose, and he struck me at the moment as being one of the greatest blockheads that I had ever met. He took his leave in a rather subdued manner, put on his gloves, and went out the door. As he was waiting to enter the lift I called out and asked him whether he would like to drink a glass of beer with some of the captains and myself later on in the evening. He stood still in surprise. I observed him furtively and saw a gleam come into his eyes. I knew I had persuaded him that I was too afraid of him to dare to quarrel, in spite of the meanness of what he had done. He apparently thought that I wanted to get on better terms with him than before, and I found out afterward that my instinct was right. At any rate, he agreed to meet me later on in the restaurant of the Woolworth Building. The door of the lift closed with a bang, and Dr. Scheele departed with a vision of the long-desired little country house, on the heights of New Jersey above the sea, which he would now be able to purchase. At least, he thought he would.

When I returned to my office, my assistants had gone, and I threw myself into a chair to work out a plan of action. I was still certain that it would not do to let the man get away with blackmail, for he would only return the next week and ask for twice as much, and in a month his demands would be increased tenfold. Besides, if he continued to receive from me the large sums he would demand, it was still possible for him to go to the police one day for some reason that might seem to him good. The first thing to do was to prevent his cashing the check and thus crowning his first attempt at blackmail with success. I took up the receiver and telephoned to two of the captains. I gave the password *"Notleine,"* [1] and they knew that there was trouble in the air. I made a hurried appointment with them and announced that "squalls were blowing up."

Dr. Scheele turned up as arranged, though I was surprised that he did so. We sat together drinking beer and talking about a variety of things. He apparently had an itch to show me what a valuable colleague he was, and, without referring to his attempt at blackmail, he pointed out a number of things that might be done. I replied very politely, and about half an hour went by before the two captains turned up. Dr. Scheele was not acquainted with them, and neither of the sailors knew what I wanted, for of course I had not been able to discuss the matter on the telephone. They sat at a table not far away but did not greet me, so that Scheele had no idea that I knew them. When he left the room for a moment I quickly informed the captains how the land lay,

[1] Alarm cord.

and what I hoped to do with their help. In due course I took leave of Dr. Scheele in the street and went off to my hotel not far away in Manhattan. Scheele, like the captains, lived near Hoboken on the other side of the Hudson.

The chemist crossed on the ferry, followed by the sailors. He strolled to and fro, and when he reached a dark corner near one of the large landing planks, one of the captains, a man of vast size, suddenly loomed up in front of him and said calmly:

"Give me the check you squeezed out of the captain today, or you'll get a sock on the jaw that'll send you whizzing down this plank."

Scheele swiftly looked round, but there was not a soul in sight. He started back when he saw the resolute and angry face of Captain Wolpert staring at him in the darkness, drew the check out of his pocket, and handed it over. Wolpert continued to stand there, powerful and threatening, while the chemist clung to a plank with both hands.

"Of course," said Wolpert, "you can go to the police now, but I don't expect they'll pay you the same monthly salary as you're getting from the firm of Gibbons. In any case, we've still got a disgruntled Irishman or two who, if you'll pardon my saying so, would find it a pleasure to tickle your stupid head with a nice, thick, iron bar. Did you really think that men like us haven't our own ways of making sure that you don't show those gold teeth of yours again?"

The ferry reached its destination, but Scheele did not move. Captain Wolpert turned sharply on his heel and walked off the ferry with an angry step and his hands in his pockets.

I received the check back the next morning. We realized that we had played a dangerous game, for though Scheele was apparently intimidated for the time being, we could not know what he would do next. Mr. Boniface had come in answer to my summons, and I asked him to keep an eye on things as far as the police were concerned, and to give us immediate warning if Scheele should denounce us. Boniface,

who had just "killed" another deal for us, stuck his hands
in his pockets, looked up at the ceiling, and said:

"Captain, there are a lot of wicked people in New York.
But I am going to do something that will enable you to put
a curb on Dr. Scheele."

He went away, and a few days later I knew what he had
done.

Scheele had one weakness. He was fond of women, so
fond of them that he was ready to make a fool of himself
if they were only young and pretty. Mr. Boniface knew this,
and drew up his plans accordingly. In order to understand
his scheme, it must be mentioned that there is a law in
America which can often be taken advantage of for strange
ends. This law exacts high penalties for seduction, which is
only just. But when an individual has a grudge against somebody else, the law can be exploited with an ease which renders it a farce, though a dangerous one.

Mr. Boniface had, as I have said, a varied clientele, which
included a pretty young girl who was useful in more ways
than one, and who was by no means unwilling to do Mr.
Boniface a good turn. Mr. Boniface was also on good terms
with the police, and was particularly friendly with a certain
detective who had been of service to him on a number of
occasions.

One day when Dr. Scheele was crossing by the Hudson
ferry, this girl was also on board and happened to drop her
umbrella. Scheele picked it up, and the acquaintance thus
begun soon ripened into friendship. In a day or two he had
to go on a journey, and he invited her to accompany him.
He possessed a venerable Ford, in which he and the girl
drove out of town. When he had left the skyscrapers of New
York behind, he stepped on the gas and gave himself up to
pleasurable thoughts of what was to come. Suddenly a man
was seen standing at the side of the highway. As soon as the
girl caught sight of him she began to scream and wave her
arms wildly in the air. Dr. Scheele was astonished, slowed
down, and asked the girl what was the matter. The man in

the road put up his hand and stopped the car. Out jumped
the girl, shrieking that her companion had tried to seduce
her and she wanted to ring up the police. The man announced that he *was* a police official and that he had stopped
the car because of the girl's screams. He also told Scheele
that he was under arrest. Scheele was speechless. He argued
with the detective, who at last let him go after he had used
all his powers of persuasion and had handed over a note
for a large sum in order to stop the matter going any further.
He continued his journey, pondering on the wickedness of
the world.

When he returned and appeared once more in my office,
Mr. Boniface was also present and kept up the comedy. He
told Scheele that it had come to his ears that a girl had
consulted a *very* celebrated New York lawyer about an attempt made by a certain Dr. Scheele to seduce her. He, Boniface, was employed by this lawyer to find Scheele. The girl
had also asserted that her would-be seducer had bribed a
police official, and, to cut a long story short, it lay in Mr.
Boniface's power to send Dr. Scheele to prison. Mr. Boniface, however, came to an agreement with Scheele: "If you
don't say anything, I won't say anything either." So Scheele
held his tongue and continued to manufacture his detonators.

The clouds, however, were gathering above our heads,
and things were beginning to get awkward. The "cigar"
business was getting too hot for us. I was rung up in the
middle of the night in my hotel bedroom and I recognized
the voice of Mr. Boniface at the other end. He did not tell
me what was wrong, but gave me a rendezvous where I could
meet him on the following morning before I went to the
office. I turned up punctually and heard from Boniface that
since the previous evening the New York police had been
manifesting feverish activity. The docks were swarming with
detectives, looking for a band of men who were placing
bombs on ships. Boniface was sure of his facts, for he had

got them from a confederate at Police Headquarters. We
walked past the docks, discussing the possible reasons for
these sudden measures, and my eye lit on the front page of
The New York Times, which I had just bought. We were
in for it! The newspaper announced with large and sensa-
tional headlines that when the empty hold of the steamer
Kirk Oswald was being swept out in Marseilles Harbor, a
peculiar little tube had been found, which on closer examination proved to be an extremely dangerous incendiary bomb.
This bomb must have been deposited while the boat was
moored at New York, and it was at once obvious how the
numerous conflagrations at sea during the last few months
had been caused. The paper announced at the same time
that the whole Secret Service department of the New York
Police was at work to seize the miscreants, and that a clue
was being pursued which offered good prospects of success.

I remembered that my men really had placed a bomb
on the *Kirk Oswald,* but I also knew that the steamer was
destined for Archangel. It was clear to me that she had received fresh orders on the way and had taken her cargo to
Marseilles instead, and that the bomb had not gone off because we had timed it to explode at a later stage on her long
journey to Archangel.

I had an appointment that morning in the lobby of my
hotel, and, as I left, I saw that I was being watched. Two
men, whom I had seen in the lobby, were following me. I
drove to a remote quarter of the town and saw that I was
not mistaken, for I was still being shadowed. As I walked
along, the two men kept on my tracks, at a suitable distance,
and when I saw a taxi and had ascertained that there was
no other car anywhere near I jumped in and drove off. I
hastened back to my office by a devious route, "liquidated"
E. V. Gibbons Inc., and shut up shop. It was necessary to
disappear for a time, and after we had hurriedly arranged
how to keep in touch my staff scattered in all directions. I
stayed at a quiet watering-place not far from New York and

awaited events; but nothing happened. Since no more bombs were being laid, the police had no opportunity of making a discovery. Still, I felt a "need of privacy."

* * * *

His missions accomplished, Von Rintelen was recalled to Germany. Posing as a Swiss businessman, he sailed for Holland, but was intercepted by the British. By then, they had cracked the new German code and they were watching for Von Rintelen. This he learned when Admiral Sir Richard Hall, chief of British Naval Intelligence, showed him a decoded copy of the very telegram that had recalled him.

During that interview, Admiral Hall's chief aide, Lord Herschell, remarked that British Intelligence also had a copy of a telegram sent to Count Spee, commander of a German cruiser squadron that had been cornered and annihilated by British battle cruisers off the Falkland Islands on December 8, 1914.

Von Rintelen was sent to a British concentration camp, but when the United States joined the war, the British summarily shipped him to America, there to stand trial for the acts of sabotage that he had engineered a few years earlier. Treated as a federal prisoner, Von Rintelen was sentenced to four years in the penitentiary at Atlanta. The war had ended when he finished his term and he returned to Germany, where he later wrote his memoirs under the title of *The Dark Invader*.

Along with his own experiences, Von Rintelen was able to supply an even more astonishing afterpiece, the story behind that coded telegram to Count Spee. Ten years after he had heard it mentioned, Von Rintelen learned the answer to one of the grandest deceptions in all naval history, and the account that follows is exactly as he tells it.

* * * *

That telegram to Count Spee! For years the business tormented me. I puzzled and worried over it while I was a prisoner of war, and later in the jails and penitentiaries of America, to which the hard-hearted and unromantic diplomacy of the British had consigned me when America also declared war against us. Again and again this one memory bobbed up out of all that had happened to me from my capture in 1915 onwards, and again after my return from captivity in 1921, at the time of the invasion of the Ruhr and the inflation, and would not leave me in peace. The telegram to Count Spee! What was behind it? What was the truth about it? How often I had racked my brains with this question!

At last, one day towards the end of 1925, when at the request of the Foreign Office I went to London to fly a very discreet kite and sound the Admiralty as to the possibility of our sending a Naval Attaché to the Embassy once more, I sent up my card to Lord Herschell, who had in the meantime become Lord-in-Waiting-in-Ordinary and had his official residence in Buckingham Palace.

"His Lordship is spending the Christmas holidays in the Isle of Wight, at his house at Bembridge," a gold-laced footman informed me.

A couple of days later a charming invitation arrived "to a bowl of punch in Bembridge, in memory of old days together in the War."

Lord Herschell was standing on the pier, of course. "Hullo, old man!" he called out, and therewith the ice was broken. It was two old friends that drove through the silent winter landscape this Christmas of 1925. The trees were glittering with hoar-frost. Thank heaven his Lordship's motorcar was heated. . . .

It was not till after dinner, after much excellent vintage port, which loosens a man's tongue so admirably, that I said:

"Tell me, Herschell, how did that telegram to Count Spee, the Admiral commanding our cruiser squadron, come to be sent? That time in 1915, when we were at the Army and Navy Club, we got off the subject. Now in 1925 we must go on at the point where we stopped then."

And now, in a rapid survey, I was treated to the whole

sad, heartrending story of the events which led to the destruction of the splendid squadron, which included the
Scharnhorst, the *Gneisenau,* the *Nürnburg* and the *Leipzig,* and of the meticulous and frenzied labors of the Admiralty, till the last meshes of the net had been woven, into
which Admiral Spee *inevitably* fell.

Lord Herschell could no longer remember quite all the
details after so many years. Not every one of the many
moves in the game which he began to describe on this evening can stand examination before the bar of naval history,
but in general his account was correct. Considering the
continual movements of the units of the British battle-
cruiser squadron, from the North Sea to the Mediterranean,
from the Irish Sea to the Atlantic, to the West Indies, and
the Antilles, mostly for the purpose of misleading our High
Seas Fleet, Lord Herschell would have needed to be a prod-
igy of memory to be able to recall every detail accurately on
the spur of the moment.

Before I recount the amazing, and to me most profoundly
depressing, story which Lord Herschell told me on this
Christmas Eve, the reader shall be given a short conspectus
of how things looked to us of the Admiralty Staff in Berlin
at the time.

After the destruction of Admiral Cradock's squadron
in the naval battle off Coronel on November 1st, 1914, the
time was close at hand when Count Spee was to round Cape
Horn with his completely intact squadron, appear in the
Atlantic, and, before doing anything else, to pick up the
ships that had been sent out to him with coal and provisions
at the agreed places.

There appeared to be three possibilities:

Either he would send his cruisers out separately with instructions to terrorize British merchant shipping, as the
Emden and, later, our auxiliary cruisers did. That would
have compelled the British Admiralty to send forth, and
subsequently disperse all over the seven seas, an enormous

number of cruisers of every class, while it was just these fast cruisers that were so urgently needed in the North Sea, for reconnoitering purposes.

Or again, Count Spee might keep his squadron together and engage the main body of the enemy cruisers, which were presumably somewhere in the Atlantic, or possibly in the West Indies, in a battle, the issue of which, to judge by events so far, was likely to be favorable to our squadron so long as, and only so long as, it had no really superior forces, i.e., modern battle-cruisers, to encounter. But that possibility—so they reasoned in Berlin—did not need to be reckoned with, because the English would not be so ready to risk a reduction in the number of the battle-cruisers stationed in the North Sea, in view of the proximity of our own battle-cruisers and the main body of the High Seas Fleet.

Finally, it was open to Count Spee to avoid engaging with the enemy in any form for the present and try to slip back home. In this case he could reckon on the High Seas Fleet's taking every care to provide suitable cover for him either to the north or to the west of Scotland or off the coast of Norway. Plans for this had been drawn up by the Admiralty Staff and the High Command of the Fleet.

This sketch gives, I think, in general a fair account of the way in which people at home conceived the position out on the high seas, and were justified in forecasting them —or, rather, in hoping they would turn out if Fate were kind; not more than that!

But the event was to be very, very different. Everything of which we had thought with such pride, such quiet faith, was destined to come tumbling down about our ears.

And now for Lord Herschell's version of the story.

"Admiral Spee was cruising with his squadron somewhere about the seven seas, and London could discover no reliable clue as to his whereabouts. The British Admiralty was, however, perfectly aware of the danger the existence of his squadron constituted to British shipping, and proceeded with its iron logic to compass its destruction. In order to join battle with the Germans with any prospect of success, it was necessary to release two battle-cruisers of the latest type. The brilliant gunnery of the *Scharnhorst* and the *Gneisenau,* which formed the kernel of Spee's squadron, could not otherwise be dealt with. Further, it was essential to try to discover where Spee would be on a given day, if the two battle-cruisers were really to be brought into action. As far as that was concerned, their plans were ready.

"But, to begin with, two British dreadnought cruisers had to be released from other duties. This had to be done unobtrusively, for if the German Naval Command got wind of the fact that two British cruisers were leaving the North Sea and making for the Atlantic it would be bound to conclude—so they said to themselves in London—that this trip had to do with Count Spee, and that had to be avoided at all costs.

"Due weight was given to the fact that the German Navy was fully aware that the majority of the British battle-cruisers were in the North Sea, while two of them had been sent off to the Mediterranean, where they remained stationed not far from the Dardanelles, in order to block any possible exit of the *Goeben* into the Mediterranean. It was still regarded as a possibility in London that this powerful German battle-cruiser would try to slip through to Pola in order to give a stiffening to the Austrian fleet. In these circumstances it was, as I have said, impossible to dispatch two battle-cruisers without more ado to chase Admiral Spee; their disappearance from their moorings would immediately have been observed by the ubiquitous German agents. Accordingly it had to be concealed; that was the essential condition of success. This could only be managed by cunning, and cunning was Admiral Hall's department.

"He had a brilliant idea. He got two new cruisers built at

an English dockyard. The job was started and carried out in complete secrecy, and the two new cruisers were all ready within a few weeks. There they were, all painted gray, with their great funnels and heavy guns pointing menacingly from their armored turrets. But they weren't battle-cruisers at all, only wooden dummies, and they were hardly finished when two powerful tugs appeared on the scene, flung their hawsers across, and one dark night towed the two wooden monsters out to sea. Officers stood on the bridge of each tug, scanning the horizon with powerful glasses for signs of an enemy ship. If anything of a suspicious nature hove in sight the smoke-screens at once got busy; for the one great condition of the success of this wheeze was that the existence of the decoys should remain an absolute secret.

"They proceeded through the Bay of Biscay, past Gibraltar, and through the Mediterranean all the way to the Aegean, where the two real battle-cruisers, the *Invincible* and the *Inflexible,* were at anchor, and had been for weeks, in full view of the islanders, among whom were a couple of men whose main occupation at that moment was to keep a sharp lookout to see whether they were still there.

"At this point the two tugs arrived—again on a dark night, of course—with the decoys in tow, which they brought right alongside of the cruisers. The wooden ships were soon riding at anchor exactly like their prototypes; seen from the shore, from the islands, they were indistinguishable from the two genuine cruisers. They too—exactly resembling their prototypes in every respect—were surrounded by a dense crowd of torpedo- and patrol-boats, to prevent mines and torpedoes from doing any damage to their valuable selves and, which was of the greatest importance, keep inquisitive eyes at a distance.

"The decoy ships were still rocking on the waves, having not yet dropped anchor, when the two real battle-cruisers moved off under the cover of darkness. They plowed their way unobserved through the waves of the Mediterranean;

and the German Intelligence Service never suspected that two dangerous enemies, infinitely superior in strength, were now on Admiral Spee's tracks. The two cruisers hurried past Gibraltar at full speed and turned sharply to the south-west."

Here Lord Herschell broke off.

"It's late, and you must have something else to think about now. Some day I'll show you round the house; you'll find lots of mementoes which I feel sure will interest you. . . . Incidentally, we shall be seeing each other again in London the day after tomorrow. Admiral Hall has invited me to make a third when he sees his old enemy of the war again for the first time."

Admiral Sir Reginald Hall had been the first person in London to whom I had paid my respects. I called on him the day after my arrival. The old attendant at the Admiralty (with whom I had had that little difficulty in August, 1915, about signing the visitors' book, and who was surprised and delighted to see me again on this occasion) informed me that Admiral Hall had (in the interval) become a Member of Parliament and was probably to be found in the House of Commons.

Sir Reginald immediately telephoned to Lord Herschell asking him to join us at lunch at the Army and Navy Club, the very same club in whose comfortable rooms we had spent a short time together once before.

My meeting with Admiral Hall was one of the greatest experiences of my life since my return from the War and captivity. The way the old gentleman put his hands on both my shoulders, and looked me straight in the eyes, honestly and unaffectedly glad to see before him such a picture of health and vigor, who had thrown off those four terrible years in American jails and penitentiaries as if they were nothing; the way this typical sailor, whose snow-white hair gave him a venerable air, stretched out his hand towards me—just exactly as Chief of the Naval Staff, Admiral Zenker, had done a few weeks before in Berlin—broke the ice instantaneously and blew away every trace of the old enmity. My dumb resentment against this man who had done me so much injury and changed the whole course of my life was buried forever from that moment. And he, moved, no doubt, by a silent desire to make up for the past, has been a staunch friend and a genius of good counsel to myself and my daughter ever since.

That is England!

That day the three of us, Admiral Hall, Lord Herschell, and myself, sat in the same club, in the same corner of the same room, in the same chairs in which we had sat ten years before, and exchanged war memories.

Lord Herschell, of course, at once introduced the topic of our Christmas Eve conversation in the Isle of Wight, the subject on which I was so intensely curious, namely, the story of Count Spee.

"Captain Rintelen is dying to know why our two battle-cruisers sailed southwest into the Atlantic."

"Yes, why on earth?" I chimed in. "They must already have known where Admiral Spee's squadron was."

"We knew where he would be," said Lord Herschell, looking across at Admiral Hall.

The Admiral's eyes were staring in front of him. "I had telegraphed to him," he said quietly. "I had telegraphed to him to let him know where our battle-cruisers would meet him, and all I can tell you is that he turned up."

I pushed my chair back a little from the table and laughed. "Really, Sir Reginald, it's rather unkind of you to pull a poor defeated enemy's leg like that. Do you expect me to believe that?"

As I looked at the Admiral's grave face I at once realized instinctively that what Lord Herschell had hinted to me was the truth. But I still did not understand. How could Hall have telegraphed to Count Spee? What did it mean? It was all completely beyond me. Then Admiral Hall began:

"We never do things by halves. We had already taken care that the two cruisers should not miss their objective.

We knew what we were doing. I have already told you
that we were in possession of the German code. You must
get that firmly into your head if you are ever to understand the story I'm going to tell you.

"It stood to reason that Spee's squadron was bound to
turn up somewhere sooner or later, and everything pointed
to the west coast of South America. The surmise proved
correct. On All Soul's Eve, 1914, the horrifying news
reached London that Count Spee had destroyed Admiral
Cradock's squadron off Coronel. He had steamed away
from the scene of battle in the direction of Valparaiso, and
the news of his arrival was, of course, at once cabled to us.
We knew that he had gone ashore with his officers and had
been welcomed by the German colony. So Count Spee is
now in Valparaiso: please hold on to that firmly for a moment."

Hall now began to construct a diagram on the table with
the aid of a variety of objects.

"Here is Valparaiso, here are our two cruisers, and there
is Berlin. Now pay attention. Here is Berlin: Count Spee
is at Valparaiso. Here are our two cruisers; there is Berlin,
and in Berlin is my man."

"Your man, Admiral?"

"Yes, my man," he said calmly; "my agent. I had instructed him to find out the exact procedure by which telegrams were sent to the German cruisers abroad. He had
informed me that the procedure was quite simple. When
such a telegram was to be sent, an Admiralty messenger
went to the head office and sent it. They used special
forms for such telegrams in Berlin, didn't they, and before
a wire of this sort could be sent it had to be stamped by
the Admiralty and the Censor's Office? I don't know how
my agent managed it, and I don't believe I should have
been very much interested if I had; all I knew was that he
had procured the required stamps and forms. Or they may
have been forged ones. Who knows?

"You've not forgotten, I hope, that Admiral Spee and his squadron are anchored off Valparaiso.

"Well, then, the moment I heard that he had arrived there I instructed my agent in Berlin to act. He had been carrying a telegram we had sent him from London about with him for some weeks. The telegram was in the German code; it contained strict and definite orders to Admiral Spee to proceed to the Falkland Islands with all speed and destroy the wireless station at Port Stanley."

"You needn't tell me the rest of the story, Sir Reginald," I said with profound emotion. "What followed I know from my service on the Admiralty Staff at Berlin."

After a short discussion in Valparaiso with the German Minister to Chile, Count Spee summoned his Chief of Staff and the commanders of his cruisers to an immediate conference. They all tried to dissuade him from carrying out the plan which he unfolded to them, which was to round Cape Horn and make for the Falklands. His Chief of Staff pointed out that such a route involved an unnecessary risk of attracting the attention of hostile forces, and that the squadron might be rendered *hors de combat* as the result of encountering the enemy in superior force, and hence, through the absence of any possibility of refitting, become useless for any further operations.

Spee told no one that he had received a secret telegram addressed to "The Admiral Commanding the Squadron —personal," and merely declared his intention of carrying out his plan. He was acting, as he supposed, on his instructions.

The death-struggle of the German squadron against the superior forces of the enemy lasted only a few hours. . . .

At home, at Admiralty Headquarters, it was a standing mystery how the two squadrons—the German under Admiral Spee, the English under Admiral Sturdee—could possibly have got at each other across so many thousands of sea miles within less than twenty-four hours. There must be something sinister and altogether mysterious behind it.

To the official report of the disaster furnished by the senior surviving German officer, Commander Pochhammer, the Kaiser appended the following manuscript note:

> "It remains a mystery what made Spee attack the Falkland Islands. See Mahan's *Naval Strategy.*"

Begging your Imperial Majesty's pardon, Count Spee had received definite and unambiguous instructions to proceed to the Falkland Islands. Only, this order came from London, not from the Admiralty Staff in Berlin, still less from your Imperial Majesty.

And yet Count Spee had his chance. He might not merely have duped an enemy many times his superior in guns, but actually have put Admiral Sturdee and his squadron out of action for a long time, even if he could not actually destroy them.

Early on the morning of December 8th, 1914, the German scouts discovered that right inside Port Stanley were two British battle-cruisers, which had only arrived during the previous day, the *Invincible* and the *Inflexible,* also three armored cruisers, all of them occupied in coaling, with hardly any steam up.

If only he had without a moment's thought sacrificed one of the squadron's tenders, the *Seydlitz* for instance— the name alone suggests it!—and sunk it so as to block the narrow opening and then turned every gun he had, especially those of the *Scharnhorst* and the *Gneisenau,* on the British as they lay there with the colliers alongside—the whole of the harbor would have gone up in flames, with serious damage, perhaps worse; in any case the enemy squadron would have been laid up for months before repair ships and cranes could get to them from England; the *Leipzig* or the *Dresden* could have been left on guard— and those operations interfered with too. . . .

Admiral Count Spee, with his squadron intact, would have been master of the southern Atlantic. What a thought! But Fate willed otherwise.

My readers must follow me back for several years.

In my account of the conversation which I had with Admiral Hall about the Zimmermann telegram, I turned the hands of the clock forward. I must now put them back to that evening in 1915, when I had just been captured and was sitting with Hall and Herschell in their club—the Junior United Services Club, I think it was.

When we left we went straight to Lord Herschell's rooms, where we had a quick whisky, and Herschell sat at the piano and played Wagner. Hall then took me by the arm and said:

"I'm afraid you must go now. There are two men waiting for you outside."

The two men were detectives, and they took me to the nearest Military Police station, where I was given a room which was partitioned off from the office. I sat down on one of the beds. I learned later that these beds were there to accommodate officers on leave who were found in the streets dead "tight." As I walked up and down, the officer in charge said to me:

"Why don't you go home? Haven't you got any lodgings?"

I pondered this remark and realized that he took me for an English officer who had been found in the street, and would be better off having his sleep out at the police station. It took me some time to think out the possible consequences of his mistake, and I came to the conclusion that it might be dangerous to leave at night when the streets of London were swarming with military patrols. Morning came at last, and as I lay on the bed I heard the officer who was being relieved say:

"There's another one at the back, but he'll soon be going."

I did not give him the lie, and prepared to take my departure. I picked up my hat, said, "Good morning," and was outside.

I knew London like a book, and was familiar with the bus routes, so I waited for the next bus which went to the Mansion House, where I could change for London Bridge. I knew that there was a tram terminus on the south bank of the Thames, not far away, and that I could get a tramcar which passed alongside the docks. If I kept my eyes open, I was bound to see a Swedish steamer, and it would not be difficult to get on board. What happened then would depend on circumstances. Perhaps I should find someone who would help me to hide until we reached Swedish territory.

As I sat on the top deck of the bus which was to take me to freedom, I thought everything over, and suddenly a black, impenetrable wall seemed to interpose itself between me and my plan. I was done. I was in a state of nervous exhaustion after the last few weeks in New York, the crossing, and the struggle with Hall and his men. I was finished. I find it impossible at this late date to give a completely plausible explanation of my next action. I cannot give any details, or say what possessed me. I saw something from the top of the bus. . . . I think it was a stockbroker of my acquaintance walking down to the office this fine morning . . . and the sheer everydayness of the happening bowled me out. I just came to a sudden resolve, got out of the omnibus and went back to the police station! When I got there no one bothered about me. I sat down on a chair and read the *Daily Mail*. Only then did it occur to me what a chance I had missed. I tried to stand up, but fell back into my chair again and could not move. The officer looked at me once or twice disapprovingly. He appeared to be displeased that I was still there. All at once I saw a second officer in the guardroom, accompanied by soldiers with fixed bayonets. He came straight up to me and said: "Are you the German Captain Rintelen?"

"Yes."

"I have orders to take you to the railway station."

As we passed the officer in charge, he looked at me with his mouth wide open. There were more things in heaven and earth than were dreamt of in his philosophy.

The Spy Who Had to Die

HISTORY has it that World War I was triggered by the assassination of the Archduke Franz Ferdinand, heir to the Austrian throne, and his wife, the Duchess of Hohenberg, during their visit to Sarajevo, the capital of Bosnia, on June 28, 1914.

Actually, the assassination of the archduke and his consort, far from being an unheard-of outrage, was the culmination of a series of such murders that had taken the lives of more than twenty members of the European ruling class at an average of better than one a year. Starting with the slaying of a French president in 1894, assassins had disposed of the Empress of Austria, the King of Italy, the King and Queen of Serbia, the King and Crown Prince of Portugal, and the King of Greece, in the order named.

They had also eliminated premiers of Spain, Greece, Russia, Egypt, and two of Bulgaria. Added to the box score were high-ranking Russians of the czarist regime, from cabinet ministers to grand dukes.

But getting on to Sarajevo, with the hunting season still open for European royalty, no monarch or prince—other than Franz Ferdinand—would have walked into what he did.

Franz Ferdinand had exactly three strikes against him. One: Bosnia was strongly Serbian and he was an Austrian.

159

Two: The Serbs were sorrowing over the 525th anniversary of the Battle of Kossovo, where they had taken an unmerciful beating from the unspeakable Turks. Three: The Austrian Army was holding maneuvers in Bosnia and the archduke was scheduled to review them.

Unfortunately for the Serbs, the Battle of Kossovo had one redeeming feature. A Serbian hero named Kobilovich had slain the victorious Sultan Murad I. Maybe Franz Ferdinand didn't see the connection or possibly he wanted to flaunt tradition. Anyway, he showed up as the representative of an oppressive regime, just 525 years after the fatal day.

All the Serbs needed was a modern Kobilovich and there were a dozen fanatical candidates planted along the archduke's route. A youth named Princip joined the Serbian immortals by shooting down the archduke at point-blank range and added the archduchess for good measure.

It was hinted that the archduke had been sent on his stupid mission to provoke the very thing that happened. Austrian officials were quick with counterclaims, stressing that the most barbarous of modern assassinations had been the slaughter of King Alexander and Queen Draga of Serbia, in the royal palace at Belgrade, eleven years before. And that had been staged by members of the Serbian nobility who were appointed to high office by the new regime.

Czarist Russia, however, sided with Serbia and would not go along with Austrian opinion. When the German Kaiser did, Europe was at war. By then, the royalties of other nations had to swallow their compunctions and team up or remain neutral as occasion demanded. But between the extremes of the regal and the radical lay the broad middle belt of the militarists, interwoven with the sinuous and sometimes invisible thread of espionage. This, according to the story that follows, could well have been the motivating force that brought on the horror and holocaust of World War I and all the terror and tribulation that civilization has suffered since.

The Spy Who Had to Die

JOSEPH GOLLOMB

EVERY government, without any exception worth noting, conducts a "war college."

I do not mean academies where fresh-faced cadets are taught the A B C of war; youths who unfold to the first sympathetic listener their plans, their hopes, their dreams; whose dress parades are pleasant public functions.

A "war college" such as I refer to is not attended by cadets, but by a picked handful of army and navy chiefs. They are crafty past masters of the science of war who study there. The public emphatically is not invited to their sessions. And the last thing in this world these students are likely to do is to divulge to outsiders the least syllable of the plans about which their studies center.

What is it that they study in a "war college"?

161

Briefly, how to win wars against any and every other nation on the globe.

The "war college" studies and hatches such plans. And the function of the secret service of any country is twofold; to keep foreign spies from learning the secrets brewing in its own "war college"; and to spy out "war college" secrets of other countries.

This is a story of the vital rôle spies play in the success or failure of a "war college."

In the early part of 1900 Alfred Redl, a major in the Austro-Hungarian army, was made chief of the secret service of the Dual Empire. He was still in his early thirties when he achieved that highly strategic position. He was a slender man of medium height, preciously groomed. His black-brown eyes, when no one was looking at them, were greedy; otherwise they were inscrutable. His nose was sharply pointed. His mouth, though thin-lipped, was vivid and sensual; but a carefully curled and pomaded mustache partly hid it.

His office in Vienna at the "Kundschafts Stelle" ("Information Department")—or as it was familiarly known, the "K.S."—was a remarkable room. It was furnished as if to be used only as the living room of an exceedingly sociable, luxury-loving man. Major Redl was all that. But although he entertained there frequently and lavishly such occasions were not always what they seemed.

Take for instance the case of Ito Onaki, a suave young Japanese. Major Redl struck up a drinking acquaintance with him one afternoon at the Central Café. On parting, Major Redl said:

"If you like a good glass of Tokay, drop in to see me tomorrow, say at about noon." He gave Onaki a number and a street.

"Charmed!" said Ito.

Neither Major Redl nor Ito had told the other his real business. But each had a shrewd idea of it. And Ito recognized the address as that of the office of the secret service of Austria-Hungary.

Nevertheless he showed up there next morning and was ushered into the room where Major Redl rose to greet him.

"What a delightful room!" Ito exclaimed.

Underfoot were thick silken rugs. The daylight was subdued by heavy brocaded window draperies except where a sharp shaft of sunlight fell athwart a luxurious armchair by the side of Major Redl's flat-topped writing desk. The air was heavy with incense. On the walls were old paintings in curiously carved ebony frames.

Major Redl with a gesture of invitation indicated the armchair by the desk. Ito sat down with the sunlight on him. His host went to a cabinet inlaid with precious woods. He took out an age-encrusted bottle of Tokay and poured out a glass for his visitor, another for himself.

Then he sat down in his own chair at the desk and, as if unconsciously, tapped the edges of a pile of important-looking papers.

"Your health, Herr Onaki!" he said, raising his glass.

"And your, Herr Korngold!" Major Redl had given that as his name.

They drank and Onaki was sincere in what he said about the wine.

"A cigarette?" Major Redl said, nodding at a gold cigarette box which stood at Onaki's hand. The top was encrusted with jewels of barbaric splendor, but the gold at the sides was smooth.

Ito declined with the apologetic smile of the non-smoker.

"Then you'll find some delicious bonbons inside that dish."

Ito raised the cover of a bit of exquisite Sèvres; and the bonbons were delicious.

The visit had lasted agreeably for about ten minutes when Major Redl's toe unseen by Ito pressed a slight bump under the thick rug where he stood chatting. Whereupon his desk telephone rang. Major Redl "answered." A short "conversation" followed. Then the host turned to his guest.

"A neighbor wants to see me urgently for about ten minutes," he apologized. "I'd hate to have you leave so soon. Won't you make yourself at home here till I come back?"

"Thank you, I will," said Ito.

Ito heard the door close with heavy dignity. His eyes craftily made sure that he was alone in the room. And outside the window a wide city square made it unlikely that anyone could even with a spyglass see Ito.

For some moments he seemed contented to rest comfortably in his armchair. Suddenly he stood up over the desk and with swift, expert fingers went through the pile of papers lying there. A large envelope was marked "Very Confidential." Inside was a sheaf of reports. Each was marked with the name of some country. Ito glanced at each only long enough to note what land the report covered. But the paper marked Servia held him. His eyes, no longer suave, darted over the contents. In his eagerness to read he thrust the paper full into the shaft of sunlight.

When ten minutes later Major Redl returned, the papers on his desk were exactly as he had left them and his guest looked up from a volume of Persian poetry.

Casual talk followed, sophisticated anecdotes, comments on women and wine. Then Ito rose and made a graceful little speech of appreciation. Major Redl escorted him to the door, and the guest left.

No one hindered his leaving. And in the street Ito's training told him after several tests he made that no one was shadowing him.

But he had, so to speak, left a broad trail behind him.

It was true he had not touched the gold cigarette box whose smooth sides were covered with minium; but there were his fingerprints clearly retained by the minium on the Sèvres bonbon dish; and an expert was already photographing them.

When Ito sat in his chair the shaft of sunlight was on his face, as I have said. In the scrollwork on two of the elaborately carved picture frames on the walls were openings in the depths of which camera lenses had been focused on Ito's face. Now two photographs were laid before Major Redl, Ito in full-face and in profile.

In the cabinet from which his host had taken the bottle of wine a phonograph had silently recorded Ito's voice.

Each sheet of the specially faked reports Ito had examined had been treated with a sensitive substance that responded to the action of light. By comparing them Major Redl knew now that it was the report on Servia which had longest engaged Ito's interest.

All these data on Ito unconsciously contributed by him were filed away in Major Redl's "Who's Who" among foreign spies operating in Austria-Hungary.

And what began as a pleasant visit to sip Tokay ended soon after for Ito with an enforced stay behind prison bars.

That room at the "K.S." as well as many other scientific and psychological traps for foreign spies was only part of Major Redl's equipment, the mechanical part of it. Even more effective was the deftness of his personality. The illustration I select may seem curious, inasmuch as it shows Major Redl getting the best of a child. But spies and detectives have told me that it is easier to fish in the well-stocked if guarded minds of adults than in the unformed, rambling, and shy mind of a child.

Major Redl called one afternoon at the house of an important state official, apparently on a social visit. He seemed distressed to find everyone out but a six-year-old son of the official and a servant.

"I'll play with little Otto till his father returns," he told the servant.

The visitor so completely entered into the child's conception of play that the servant felt it safe to withdraw to do some housework. The major even invented games. One of them consisted of a kind of hide-and-seek. Each player in turn hid an object which the other tried to find. Major Redl held up a coin.

"Now if this time you can hide this so that I can't find it, the coin is yours," the major said. "I'll give you a hint. Put it some place where your papa hides things, then I surely won't be able to find it."

"I know where!" exclaimed the child. "In this very room!"

"Good! Now I'll turn my face away while you hide your coin there."

The child won the coin. And his father went to prison as a result of what Major Redl found in the hiding place the child had thought safe.

For decades there had been bad blood between Austria-Hungary and its neighbor Servia. Peace and war between the two were in a state of delicate equilibrium. Now, Servia by itself would not have given the "war college" of Austria-Hungary any great concern. But behind Servia was its powerful ally, Russia. And allied to Russia was France with England as another probable ally.

In back of Austria-Hungary on the other hand was the German Empire.

As every schoolboy now knows, this line-up of powers made the Great War. And even in 1900 when Major Redl had charge of the secret service of Austria-Hungary, in every "war college" in Europe there was uneasy knowledge that trouble was brewing.

Taking the German General von Moltke's degree of preparedness as model, the "war college" of Austria-Hungary with General Conrad von Hötzendorf, commander-in-chief of the army, as "professor" studied particularly how best to invade Servia at the instant of war. It takes years to mature such a plan. Railroads have to be so organized, roads so built, provisions made for the transport of such masses of men, cannon, ammunition, and food that at the word of war whole armies can be moved with the swiftness of surprise.

If, however, such a movement should be delayed long enough to give the enemy time to prepare for it; or worse still if the enemy should by some means learn the details of such a plan, then, of course, it would be better that the plan should never have been born.

"Plan Three," for the invasion of Servia between Drina-mundung and Savemundung was the slowly maturing pet project of the "war college" of Austria-Hungary.

And it was Major Redl's duty to see that no one outside of the "war college" learned as much as a syllable of "Plan Three."

He succeeded apparently so well as chief of the secret service that he won promotion after promotion until he became Colonel Redl and was made member of the Prague Army Corps, and as such was a participant in the formulation of "Plan Three."

At about this time Redl took stock of himself. As a brilliant and quickly rising Austrian army officer he commanded a respectable salary. But Colonel Redl's lust for luxury was anything but respectable in proportion to his income.

Lust and luxury were with him imperative. He could hide his inner self from his closest colleague. But he made no attempt to hide from himself the fact that his appetites came first and foremost of all the loyalties he recognized.

From his own country Redl could count on only a colonel's salary. From Russia—if he chose—he could confidently expect the income of a prince.

One day there came on a visit to gay Vienna a Russian nobleman who held the purse strings of the secret service in his country. Colonel Redl, as a sort of "friendly enemy" colleague, helped to make Vienna still more gay for the visitor. Then one day the two, apparently to recuperate from too much Viennese night life, went out into the country for a stroll.

Colonel Redl led to a hilltop from which there was a fine view to be had in every direction. There was not a soul in sight. Whereupon Colonel Redl and the Russian began to talk business.

Both men were hard-headed and psychologically and

spiritually spoke the same language. At the end of several hours' talk they understood each other very well indeed.

Then the visitor went back to Russia and Colonel Redl went back to work.

Not long after this the heir to the throne of Austria-Hungary, Archduke Francis Ferdinand, visited Russia, where he was so lavishly entertained that he felt grateful. Like most royal princes he was rather out of touch with hard reality. As a graceful gesture he asked Colonel Redl that Austro-Hungarian espionage in Russia be reduced.

But just about this time a Russian colonel privately came to see an Austro-Hungarian military attaché in Warsaw. The Russian colonel, like Colonel Redl, had appetites too rich for a mere colonel's salary. So he quietly offered to sell to Austria-Hungary something that had been carefully matured by the Russian "war college."

This was a detailed plan for Russian military invasion of Germany and Austria-Hungary at the outbreak of war.

The military attaché knew, of course, of Archduke Francis Ferdinand's desire to reduce his country's spying on Russia. But these plans were far too important to pass by, the crown prince notwithstanding. So the attaché did not disturb Archduke Francis Ferdinand, but took the papers and the terms of sale of the Russian colonel directly to Colonel Redl.

Redl read them.

"Did you examine these plans?" he asked sharply.

"No, but I have an idea of how important they are," said the attaché.

Colonel Redl went to his private safe—this was in the "living room" I have described in the "K.S."—and securely locked up the papers.

"I shall cite to your superiors—discreetly, of course, but to your benefit—your keen judgment in this matter, lieutenant," Colonel Redl said softly. "You did the right thing in coming straight to me. I am sorry to inform you, however, that your Russian colonel is not a traitor as you hoped, but a charlatan. These plans for which he asks a fortune were drawn up not by the Russian 'war college,' but in his own none-too-brilliant imagination. Tell him we will have nothing to do with him."

The lieutenant was disappointed. But he need not have been. For the plans were of the highest importance. They were returned quietly and safely to the archives of the Russian "war college" whence they had been stolen.

And not long after that Colonel Redl anonymously bought a house in Vienna; two shining motors; and luxuriously furnished a private—very private—apartment in Prague.

But the Russian colonel who had offered the plans for sale was visited one night by several of his fellow officers. As regimental comrades they accorded him the privilege of blowing out his brains with his own revolver. Which he did.

There followed for Colonel Redl a long period of prosperity. Financially he flourished far beyond the knowledge of his colleagues. But he also won rapid promotion for services to his country.

One foreign spy after another was lured by him to destruction. In the year 1902 alone Lieutenant Alex von Caric went to prison for four and a half years. Paul Marstmann, "international spy," and Pietro Contini, working for the Italian "war college," were sentenced to four years in prison each. Which for a peacetime year is not a bad bag for a hunter of spies.

It was true that this success was somewhat offset by the number of distressing fatalities among Austro-Hungarian spies in Russia. Colonel Redl's men were bewildered by the bad luck that seemed to follow his field workers in the Czar's country. It was as if a curse had been laid on them in Russia.

But the staff in Austria was dazzled by the competence and success of their chief at home. He was their model, their ideal, their idol. "How would Colonel Redl do this?"

was the standard they set themselves. "What would Colonel Redl think of that?" worried secret service men who blundered.

Only for an hour one afternoon—a critical hour for Colonel Redl—did anyone's faith in the spy chief waver.

It was in 1903 during the trial of a young clerk by the name of Hekailo. He was charged with having betrayed to Russia plans which the "war colleges" of Germany and Austria-Hungary had jointly developed for a military invasion of Russia by way of Thorn.

Dr. Haberditz, a shrewd Viennese lawyer, had charge of the prosecution. Colonel Redl, as head of the "K.S.," was by his side acting as adviser and furnishing him evidence against Hekailo. Proof had been piling up against the prisoner to such an extent that two of his Austrian accomplices were uncovered and dragged into the dock along with him.

They were Major Ritter von Wienckowski, stationed at Stanislau, and Captain Acht, personal adjutant of the commander at Lemberg.

Suddenly Colonel Redl's attitude toward the prisoners changed.

"I'm afraid I've been mistaken about them," he told Dr. Haberditz. "My case against them isn't as strong as I thought."

The lawyer was puzzled.

"Colonel Redl, this is very strange indeed! I don't understand it, this sudden change of front. What does it mean?"

Colonel Redl regarded him stonily. "I'm not on trial before you, Doctor," he said.

"Perhaps not. But I feel it my duty to take up this matter with the other members of the General Staff."

Colonel Redl bit his mustache. "Give me two hours' time to look into the matter, Dr. Haberditz."

Two hours later Colonel Redl dispelled the suspicion that was dawning in Dr. Haberditz's mind. He came back with such a volume of evidence against the defendants that they were sentenced to terms from eight to twelve years in prison.

And the queer little lapse in Colonel Redl's vigor as a hunter of spies was overlooked and forgotten—until ten years later.

But Colonel Redl had had a narrow escape. For as soon as Major von Wienckowski and Captain Acht were drawn into the net with Hekailo word came quietly to Redl:

"They are two of our best men, too valuable for us to lose. You must see that they get free."

Clearly it was not from Austro-Hungarian sources that this mandate had come. And the voice of Colonel Redl's secret master was not to be disregarded. Hence the change in his attitude that had so puzzled Dr. Haberditz.

But Dr. Haberditz's threat to report this mysterious change of heart to the General Staff was equally dangerous. So Colonel Redl asked the prosecuting attorney for two hours' respite. During those two hours Redl had to do some delicate and secret bargaining.

"If I try to free von Wienckowski and Acht I shall be suspected. In that case I shall probably cease to be of any further service to you," he said to the emissary of his foreign master. "Make up your mind which is more important to you, they or I."

The emissary weighed values and referred the matter by telegraph code to St. Petersburg.

"Very well," word came back. "Von Wienckowski and Acht shall be sacrificed to save you. But in return you must betray to us two more among your best spies in Russia."

Thus the bargain was sealed. And there was added to Colonel Redl's credit in Austria-Hungary his uncovering of the three traitors, Hekailo, von Wienckowski, and Acht.

Finally the Austro-Hungarian General Staff began to feel that Colonel Redl was too brilliant a man to be wasted on even such an important position as head of the country's secret service. He was promoted to be Chief of Staff of the Eighth Army Corps stationed at Prague.

This was the corps which would have most to do with the carrying out of "Plan Three" when it came to invading Servia.

Colonel Redl was succeeded by Captain Ronge as Chief of the "K.S." Captain Ronge was a sterling officer, and almost sentimental in his worship of his predecessor's genius.

"I shall attempt to follow worthily in your footsteps, Colonel," he said. This was at a farewell to Colonel Redl. "But I am afraid I cannot fill your shoes."

Colonel Redl put his hand on Ronge's shoulders and looked proudly at the others of the "K.S." staff.

"Captain Ronge and colleagues!" he said. "My greatest achievement is the men I leave behind me at the Kundschafts Stelle!"

It was a graceful speech and true. But Colonel Redl himself did not realize how truly he had spoken—until it came home to him years later.

In addition to the organization he had raised to superb efficiency Colonel Redl left behind him several books written by him. They were all in manuscript and were not in the least for general circulation. They were manuals on how to trap foreign spies; and how to keep from being trapped while spying on foreign soil.

Then he took his new and lofty place in the "war college" of Austria-Hungary.

We come now to the year before the world-wide explosion of 1914. European "war colleges" were maturing their devastating projects. The atmosphere of Europe, as the world learned only too soon—and too late—was as dangerous as a vast storehouse of dynamite. A spark, a revolver shot would set the whole thing off.

In Vienna the secret service was watching the mails. The postal authorities were told that the government was on the lookout for smugglers. This was the reason given why secret service men opened private letters in the General Post Office, read them, and sealing them up again let the mail proceed.

What was really going on was a hunt for foreign spies.

One day the secret service men came across an envelope addressed rather oddly:

"Opera Ball, 13,
    Poste Restante,
        General Post Office,
            Vienna."

Inside was found about $2,800 in Austrian kronen—and not a word of covering letter!

The postmark was Eydtkuhnen in East Prussia, a tiny town on the Russian frontier. Eydtkuhnen! Known to the secret service as the corridor most favored by spies of half a dozen countries for the passing from one country to another.

The envelope was sealed up again and put back in its place to await its owner.

An electrician was called. Under the ledge over which the letter would be handed by the postal clerk to the person who should call for "Opera Ball, 13," a push-button was installed. From it a wire led across the street to a branch police station in the Fleischmarkt.

"The moment the letter is called for," the postal clerk was instructed, "push this button and be as slow as you can in handing over the letter."

In the police station two secret service detectives were assigned to do nothing but wait for the newly installed electric bell to ring.

They waited. They waited a week; two weeks; three; a month. Not a ring from the post office. April passed. May was almost gone. Still not a sound. And there in the post office still lay unclaimed an envelope with $2,800 in it. Had news of the trap leaked out?

On the eighty-third day of waiting one of the secret service men was negligent enough to go out for a cup of coffee several doors from the stationhouse. The other was also out of the room washing his hands in the corridor, when he heard a sound that shocked him. The little electric bell was ringing.

Dashing back into the room, he snatched up his coat and hat and started for the general delivery window of the post office. But he made a slight detour to call out to his partner at the café.

Both hurried breathlessly over to the post office. They found no one but the clerk at the window.

"You've missed your man!" exclaimed the clerk. "He left by that door about half a minute ago."

The detectives rushed to the street just in time to see a taxi turn the corner. And not another taxi in sight!

The two men looked at each other in dismay. Assigned to such a simple task, with so much depending on it, they had bungled it! The fact that they caught the number on the taxi's license plate cheered them but little. The fox would know enough to double on his trail at the first convenient corner. What would Colonel Redl have said to such stupidity?

"What rotten luck!"

But it turned out that the two men had little reason to complain. As one of them later expressed it when I talked to him in Innsbruck, "We had hunter's luck that day (*Jägergluck*)!"

For, twenty minutes later a taxi rolled by them and there on the license plate was the number they had noted.

They hailed the taxi. "I saw you drive off with my brother-in-law twenty minutes ago," said one of the detectives. "Where did you take him?"

"To the Kaiserhof Café," the driver said.

"Take us there."

On the way to the Kaiserhof the two men searched the taxi. They were products of the Redl system of training and, though they had little reason to hope for results in this case, they burrowed between the cushions of the taxi largely from force of habit, the habit of minute search.

They found the sheath of a pocketknife, a little sack of gray suède.

But at the Kaiserhof Café they found no one but waiters. And no one had come there within an hour and a half.

Again the detectives bewailed their luck; and again luck favored them. Near the café was a taxi rank. An old man who got small coins for opening carriage doors remembered that a gentleman had taken a taxi there some twenty minutes before and Hotel Klomser was where the gentleman told the taxi driver to take him.

To the Hotel Klomser went the two secret service men.

One of them sat down at a table of periodicals near the door and pretended to read. The other approached the dignitary who presides at the entrance to every continental hotel, the *Portier*.

Had anyone arrived at the hotel within the half hour, asked the detective.

"Yes, several people," replied the *Portier*. "The couple for Room 5, Herr Wormser of Number 11, and the young lady in Number 21. Oh, yes, Colonel Redl also arrived. He had his usual room, Number 1."

"Do you mean *the* Colonel Redl?" one of the detectives asked.

"Colonel Redl of Prague is all I know of him."

The detective almost blushed as he thought again of what Colonel Redl would say if he learned how he and his partner had blundered that day.

He stooped and pretended to pick something up from the floor.

"Someone has lost this pocketknife sheath," he said, giving it to the *Portier*. "You might ask whose it is."

Then the detective leisurely strolled out of the hotel and, crossing the street, gave himself over to an idle study of the weather.

His partner inside seemed engrossed in a copy of *Simplicissimus*, smiling at what he read.

From the interior of the hotel a dapper gentleman strolled over to the *Portier's* desk and laid down the key to

Number 1. The *Portier* touched his gold-braided cap.

"Pardon, Colonel, but have you perhaps lost this pocket-knife sheath?" he asked.

The gentleman looked at it and took it. "Yes, thanks, I must have dropped it——" There was only a look of idle speculation as he began. His leisure, his whole manner was that of a man very much at ease in this world.

But suddenly the detective over the top of his *Simplicissimus* saw the face of the gentleman grow deathly white.

He remembered now where he had lost that sheath—in the taxicab where he had used his penknife in opening the envelope he had called for at the post office. Later when in the second cab he took out his penknife again he found that he had lost the sheath. If now the *Portier* gave it to him, what did it all mean? Who was it knew enough to bring the sheath to the Hotel Klomser?

His posture perhaps a little too stiff for one who was trying to appear at ease, the gentleman strolled out of the hotel.

With the alertness of the born detective he had noted the stranger reading *Simplicissimus*. He would have wondered, had he noted the further fact that the reader of the famous satirical weekly had himself turned pale.

And as soon as the gentleman left the hotel this detective hurried to the telephone booth and tightly closed the door.

"1233408!"

He was given his number quickly, for it was that of the "Kundschafts Stelle."

Captain Ronge, successor to Colonel Redl, himself answered the telephone. What he heard made him snap:

"Blockhead! Do you realize what you are trying to make me believe?"

Nevertheless it was Captain Ronge himself who rushed in a taxi to the General Post Office. Here he secured the receipt signed by the man to whom had been delivered the envelope marked "Opera Ball, 13."

The name signed was unknown to Captain Ronge. That didn't matter; a false name was to be expected. Back to the "Kundschafts Stelle" Captain Ronge drove.

From a well hidden file he took down several handsomely bound little books in manuscript—the books written in Colonel Redl's own hand. Captain Ronge opened one of them entitled, "Organisation der Auskundschaftung fremder Militärverhältnisse und die Abwehr fremder Spionage im Inlande."

On a leaf of this book telling how to guard Austro-Hungarian military secrets and at the same time ferret the secrets of other "war colleges," Captain Ronge laid the signed receipt for "Opera Ball, 13."

There was no evading the conclusion. The handwriting on the receipt and the handwriting of the manuscript were one!

"Good God!" Captain Ronge whispered.

Meanwhile Colonel Redl was strolling apparently in a mood of leisure down the Herrengasse. At the corner of Strauchgasse he looked into a haberdasher's window.

Yes, in the mirror he saw coming in his direction the man who had been reading *Simplicissimus* and another he had observed standing across the street from the hotel.

He, Colonel Redl, Chief of Staff of the Eighth Army Corps, had been trailed from the General Post Office; to the taxi rank where he had changed vehicles; to Hotel Klomser. The pocketknife sheath had been traced to him. And now he was being shadowed in his own city with a technique he had himself taught his men in the "Kundschafts Stelle!" No wonder his face was ghastly.

He must gain a little time to think. He must throw the men off his trail if only long enough to catch a train for Prague and destroy the contents of his desk in the apartment there. Whether even lack of documentary evidence would now save him, he did not allow himself to speculate. He was drowning and one catches at straws at such a time.

Down the Wollnerstrasse he turned. The men in his

wake also turned the corner. Colonel Redl put his hand into an inside pocket and taking out some papers he tore them into bits. He did not look to see what he was tearing up. It did not matter; additional evidence could not increase his peril. Time, a little time, a few minutes' gain on his shadows, was all he could hope for. If they stopped to pick up the bits of torn paper—he had trained his men to do that—he might shake them off long enough to escape into the Old Exchange Building which had exits on three streets.

Only one of the men stopped to pick up the bits of paper. With these in his pocket this man rushed in a taxi to the "Kundschafts Stelle." There Captain Ronge pieced together the papers Colonel Redl had torn up.

They were receipts for letters registered and sent to Brussels, Lausanne, and Warsaw. The addresses were all familiar to Captain Ronge.

One was the joint office in Brussels of the Russian and French secret services. Another was the foreign headquarters of the Italian secret service. The third was that of one of the principal offices of the Russian secret service.

"My greatest achievement," Colonel Redl had said, "is the men I leave behind me at the 'Kundschafts Stelle'!"

One of them was now dogging his steps; and in a little while there were again two. Tricks seemed useless now; escape hopeless. Colonel Redl turned to go back to his hotel.

A hearty hello arrested him. It was Dr. Victor Pollack, a close friend of Colonel Redl's and one of the leading prosecutors in espionage cases.

"We dine at the Riedhof, Alfred!" Dr. Pollack exclaimed.

Redl nodded acceptance. "I'll go dress and meet you at the Riedhof at seven," he said.

As yet no one interfered with him and at seven o'clock exactly he entered the dining room of the Riedhof, immaculate and glittering in his uniform. But as he sat down his friend noticed that Redl was pale.

"What is it, Alfred?" Pollack asked.

Redl did not have to exert his talent as an actor; the depression he felt was genuine. Nevertheless he was playing a game, perhaps his last.

He leaned over the table and began to confess to his friend. He confessed moral lapses, degeneracy, a strain of insanity in his family and a fear that he was himself going insane. He confessed enough to justify gloom in any man, but he said not a word of the real reason for his depression.

"Do something for me, Victor, my friend!" he entreated softly. A waiter was hovering about and without consciously suspecting him Colonel Redl spoke only when the man was away. "I fear for my sanity at this very moment. I want to go back to Prague—at once—tonight! To my little apartment. I shall feel quiet there. Then you can come and take me to a sanitarium. But I don't want to go to Prague alone. You know Chief of Police Gayer. Ask him to send one of his detectives with me as escort!"

Dr. Pollack rose. "That's easy, Alfred," he said. "I'll be back in a few minutes."

He went to the telephone booth and called up the Chief's home. Herr Gayer was still at his office, he was told. Dr. Pollack called up police headquarters and found Gayer there.

"You're working late today, my friend," Pollack said.

"Important case," Gayer said.

"Well, it's about Colonel Redl I want to speak to you," Pollack went on.

"You're dining with him at the Riedhof?"

"Why, how do you know?"

"Oh, I learned it accidentally. What can I do for Colonel Redl?"

Dr. Pollack told him what Colonel Redl wished.

Gayer seemed to sympathize. "But I can spare no one to-night," he said. "Calm the Colonel and tell him to come to me first thing in the morning."

The secret service man in the guise of a waiter had been listening to Dr. Pollack speaking over the telephone. He was puzzled. He knew whom Dr. Pollack had called up and who it was that promised to do as Colonel Redl wished. Did it mean that the affair was to be hushed up? Then the scandal was so great that there must be no scandal.

But Colonel Redl's face, when Dr. Pollack reported what Gayer had promised, showed no relief.

He said little during the rest of the meal. An orchestra—and it seems to me that nowhere in the world as in Vienna can orchestras woo the heart with such light-hearted charm—was playing a Waldteufel waltz. Redl seemed to be listening to it.

In reality he was brooding over his latest failure. His hope had been that the Chief of Police would send him a detective as escort; that the secret service seeing this would be content to let the detective be the sole watch over him that night. Then there would be only a city detective to outwit.

At eight-thirty Dr. Pollack saw his friend to his room at the Hotel Klomser and left him apparently in a more cheerful frame of mind.

Meanwhile at the Grand Hotel General Conrad von Hötzendorf, Commander-in-Chief of the Austro-Hungarian army, was host to a gay party. French vintage champagne; the famous string ensemble of the Grand Hotel in those days; faces of lovely Viennese women; good news sent to him by some of his spies in Paris—they all helped to make the architect of "Plan Three" feel pleased with life that evening.

In the midst of dinner a waiter brought him the card of General August Urbanski von Ostromiecz. "Can I speak to you privately?" was written on the back. "I am in the office of the hotel manager."

General von Hötzendorf excused himself to his guests.

"General, who is it?" exclaimed a lovely lady. "I'm jealous!"

"It may be something pleasant I shall share with you," the general smiled.

In the manager's private office he found General Urbanski pacing agitatedly up and down.

"As serious as that?" von Hötzendorf asked with a bit of banter.

"General!"

The head of the united secret services of Austria-Hungary told the Commander-in-Chief his news. He told it with the brevity of a soldier making his report. He spoke in so hushed a tone that the strains of the orchestra drifting into the room seemed at times louder than his voice.

General von Hötzendorf seemed to be aging momentarily as he listened. His face turned livid. A fine dew broke out of his forehead.

"He must be caught!" he cried hoarsely.

"He's under surveillance!"

"He must be made to reveal the extent of his treason!"

"It shall be done!"

"Then he must die!"

General Urbanski caught up his gloves.

"And under no circumstances must the manner or reason of his death be made known!"

"I understand, General!"

"If Russia should learn that we have discovered Redl —— Oh, why doesn't that hellish orchestra stop!"

Then a thought struck him. *"Good God, if Plan Three should be known—— General, everything must take place tonight!"

"At your orders!"

"You, Captain Ronge, Major Hofer, and Wenzel Vorlicek will see to it. Then report at once!"

At the Hotel Klomser, Colonel Redl was writing in his room when at midnight there was a sharp knock on the door. Without invitation four officers in full uniform entered.

Colonel Redl, white-faced, immaculate, holding himself very straight, rose as they entered.

"I know why you come," he said slowly. "I have written it all in these letters."

"Any accomplices?"

"None."

"Your activities, how long and to what extent?"

"In my apartment in Prague you will find all the proofs."

"Colonel, have you a revolver?"

"May I borrow yours, Major?"

He was handed a Browning revolver.

"Thank you," Redl said. "Good night, gentlemen!"

The officers left without a word.

One of them posted himself across the street from the hotel. The others went to the Central Café and waited.

At five in the morning one of the two secret service men who had shadowed Colonel Redl was summoned to the café.

"Go to Colonel Redl's room at the Klomser," General Urbanski ordered. "If his door is locked, use this passkey. No matter what has happened in his room you are to raise no alarm. Report back here."

The secret service man went to the hotel and showed the night porter his badge of office. "Colonel Redl expects me to deliver this letter in person," he told him.

The detective went to Room Number One alone.

But there was no reply to his knock on the door. The detective found it unlocked and entering closed the door behind him.

The lights were on. The silk shades of two of them were so tilted that a strong light would fall on anyone who stood before the ceiling-high mirror.

On the rug before the mirror lay Redl motionless. His fingers were tight about the Browning.

The secret service man left the hotel quietly and reported to his superiors in the café.

A quarter of an hour later the telephone bell at the reception desk of the Hotel Klomser rang. The night porter answered it.

"Request Colonel Redl to come to the instrument you are using," a voice said over the wire.

"He is sleeping," protested the porter. "Who are you?"

"Do as you're told!"

The porter recognized the voice of authority and obeyed it.

It was thus that the "regrettable suicide" of Colonel Redl was made public. The world was informed that "following a long period of melancholia, Colonel Alfred Redl, Chief of Staff of the Eighth Army Corps, committed suicide last night."

But a small group was closeted with General von Hötzendorf.

"Gentlemen," he said, "I shall require of every one of you a special vow of absolute silence in the matter of Colonel Redl. Not even our Emperor must know of it!"

The newspapers of Austria-Hungary gave top space to the announcement, but made no comment. First, because they knew of no comment to make other than obituary praise. Second, the press of Austria-Hungary in those days was under the heel of the military.

A special train took General von Hötzendorf, General Urbanski and Captain Ronge to Prague where they went at once to Colonel Redl's apartment. Strong especially constructed locks on the door halted them.

Captain Ronge went in search of a locksmith and found a young fellow by the name of Wagner. "Come with me!" he ordered.

"But I don't work on Sundays," Wagner protested. "And I'm fullback on my football team which plays Union V. this morning!"

Then the young man found that he had no choice; he was drafted for "temporary military service."

He broke open the locks on Colonel Redl's doors and various strongboxes and desks. The three military men pounced on the contents. Wagner caught glimpses of maps, sketches, photographs, blueprints, reports of all kinds. He heard the oldest of the group exclaim with a sort of horror:

"How was it possible!"

And he caught a murmur of the word, "Russia."

Wagner was a good locksmith but lacked curiosity. What he had seen impressed him but little.

Because of his absence his team lost the game. Next day his captain, who during the week was assistant sporting editor on the *Prager Tagblatt,* lectured him for not showing up to play.

"I couldn't," Wagner explained. "The military made me break open some locks for them. It was Colonel Redl's apartment."

And he told his captain as much as he knew of what had happened.

The football captain was no fool. Putting together the official statement of Colonel Redl's suicide with what Wagner told him, the assistant editor realized that he had a sensation in his possession.

He took it to his editorial chief. There was no mistake, they decided, Colonel Redl must have been unearthed as a spy!

But it was a dangerous bomb for a newspaper in Austria-Hungary to handle. Truth would not protect the paper from the explosion. And yet the story was too big to let go. So this is what appeared in the *Prager Tagblatt* on Tuesday morning:

We are asked by a high authority to contradict rumors which have been spread, particularly in army circles, about the Chief of the Staff of the Prague Army Corps, Colonel A. Redl, who, as already reported, committed

suicide in Vienna on Sunday morning. The rumors are to
the effect that the colonel had been guilty of betraying
military secrets to a foreign Power, believed to be Russia. As a matter of fact, the commission of high officers
who came to Prague to carry out a search in the dead
Colonel's house was investigating quite another matter. . . .

An uproar followed; for, of course, everyone read between the lines. Reporters mobbed news sources of the
story. In Parliament there was commotion. And telegraph
wires and cables fairly sputtered as the story spread
throughout the world.

Then several months later a Servian student fired his revolver at the heir to the throne of Austria-Hungary, killing
him and his wife.

Whereupon the Great War broke out.

Hoping against hope that "Plan Three" was still a secret,
General von Hötzendorf hurled an Austro-Hungarian
army into Servia. At every point of attack the Servians, under Marshal Putnik, were there, mysteriously prepared.
Thrice von Hötzendorf tried variants of "Plan Three." And
each time he met with catastrophe.

If ghosts ever meet, thousands of Austrians killed on
Servian soil will have something to say to Alfred Redl.

But I traveled a hundred miles to ask one of the princi-
pals in this story a single question.

"Suppose Colonel Redl had refused to blow out his
brains?"

The man looked grimly across the vista of time and great
change and obviously was back to the hour of which we
had been speaking. His smile was not pleasant to see. Then
it went.

"It would not have done him any good!" he said.

A Very Special Agent

IN Colonial America it was difficult to know where military scouting ended and spying began. Nathan Hale, a former schoolteacher and captain in the Continental Army, was captured spying on the British in New York and was hanged (if one is to judge from the records and plaques) at one of several places in mid-Manhattan.

Hale's last words, "I only regret that I have but one life to lose for my country," were not only heroic, but in a sense prophetic. General Washington, himself a scout since boyhood, promptly went back to the old system of scouting and in time developed an effective chain of informants.

Of necessity, the observers worked with discretion and, even after the Revolution, the names of many secret agents were never revealed. Only those who had served as "double spies" were generally made public, in order to square them with their fellow-townsmen, who usually regarded them as Tories and commonly gave them a rather hard time.

Scouting became a small industry during the Civil War. In the early days of that conflict, ingenious Yankees who scouted the Southern States carried interesting new devices called cameras and posed as itinerant photographers to cover their secret activities.

Did those cameras excite suspicion? Absolutely not. Nobody dreamed that such newfangled contraptions could be

187

used for taking photos of defenses, troop movements, and the like. Least aware of such possibilities were the Northern spies themselves. They merely used their cameras to gain the confidence of Southern generals, who posed on verandas with their staff officers while the pretended photographers took snapshots and wrote up orders for finished prints.

The trouble was that photography was more of an art than spying in those days. So few pictures were actually developed and delivered by the fake cameramen, that the picture-takers were sought as swindlers and forced to take off beyond the Mason-Dixon line before their real game was discovered. Unhappily for the spy, photographic technology soon made the word "camera" spell "spy" in any language. Anybody taking pictures of military installations was promptly placed under arrest, even in peacetime.

Photographers were dangerous, but artists, of course, were harmless. An Englishman, Sir Robert Baden-Powell, roamed through friendly countries posing as a naturalist, making colored sketches of unusual butterflies. Luckily, nobody compared the sketches with the insects, because the markings of the wings were actually the plans of fortifications that Baden-Powell had noted and sketched first. Adapting hobbies and crafts to practical purposes so appealed to Baden-Powell that in 1908, he founded the Boy Scouts—although espionage was not a recommended activity.

Nevertheless, in the modern complexities of international intelligence and counterintelligence, even a Boy Scout might be a camouflaged secret agent, using a disguised old lady as a "drop" by slipping her a coded message while pretending to help her across the street. After all, Central Intelligence does not care how it gets its information, just so long as it gets it.

That point is well established in the story that follows, as told by that keenest of analysts, Anthony Abbot.

A Very Special Agent

ANTHONY ABBOT

YOU might call the story of George Stanley a true composite of what happened to a number of F.B.I. men, with names of men and places changed—and yet from this necessary hodgepodge emerges the true picture of what espionage work was really like. And in one place or another, to one man or another, all this really happened.

One morning in October, 1938, there came to J. Edgar Hoover's office in Washington this letter:

> I am a lawyer and trust administrator for a national bank. The international future looks dangerous to me and I want to enlist early on the democratic side. Do you think I might qualify for a post in the F.B.I.?
>
> George Stanley.

Reports about Stanley from F.B.I. investigators were mixed. On the dubious side, he had been a radical in campus activities; worse, he loved a quiet, scholarly life and, as one report phrased it, he was "overly polite."

Working as gardener, church janitor, schoolteacher, and hotel clerk he had earned three college degrees, then took a postgraduate course in psychiatry for lawyers. He was fluent in German, French, and other languages. One summer he had played in a Cape Cod theater, and his director testified:

"Although a beginner, Stanley has a rare gift for impersonation. He can turn himself into another character at will; eyes, voice, walk, posture—everything seems to change!"

The summary on him read:

"This man has intelligence and desirable special qualifications. But he would need a great deal of roughening up before he could ever make a special agent. Can it be done?"

Hoover decided to find out. In February, 1939, George Stanley entered the National Police Academy of the Federal Bureau of Investigation, where three months' training has often proved too tough for hardy men. They taught him attack and self-defense, with no holds barred; but even after mastering judo, Stanley would still murmur, "I'm terribly sorry," before knocking a man out. In his final examination he was marked excellent in visual memory, crime scene research, description, and identification; he was tops with firearms but:

"He still seems to want to make a good impression on everybody."

Perhaps work in the field would tune him up. The special agent to whom he was assigned was told to be "very hardboiled with Stanley." Soon he was fighting highjackers with bare fists in Chattanooga and shooting it out with auto thieves in San Francisco.

Meanwhile, the need for American agents abroad was becoming so urgent that the F.B.I. recalled twenty agents, picked because of general ability and knowledge of languages, for indoctrination in foreign service. At the end of the course, five men stood out, and Stanley topped them all.

"Except," an instructor reported, "that he is a little too nice and gentle for such dangerous assignments; he ought to be a lot tougher."

Nevertheless, it was decided to take a chance on Stanley, and within a week he was on his way to the most difficult field in all counter-intelligence—Japan!

What were his orders? If war came to the United States, the F.B.I. would need vast quantities of background material. For example, a day might come when one of the men, a "double agent" acting the part of a Reich operator, would meet, as coworker, with a real German spy. The man might pretend that he had worked at Nazi espionage headquarters in Tokyo. The other might then challenge him: Where were those headquarters? On which side of the street? Do you go upstairs or down? How many rooms? What pictures are behind the desk? And our agent must know the answers!

This is but one of a hundred different uses for background material. Descriptions, drawings, snapshots—a whole treasury of unrelated items, to be catalogued, indexed, and stored away against some moment yet to come when one tiny fact out of ten thousand might save an American convoy or win a victory for our army.

When he left Washington, all George Stanley had in the way of orders was, in effect: "Go get what you can—and don't get caught!" On his very first day in Tokyo he faced what seemed disaster.

There lived in a back street not far from the Ginza, a limping little cobbler who for two years had been on the F.B.I. payroll. His shop was to be Stanley's "drop." But when the amiable F.B.I. agent sauntered past the shoemaker's door, the place was dark and boarded up; the cobbler gone; no doubt already beheaded; for clearly, Stanley's contact man in Tokyo had been discovered.

What the special agent then decided to do is probably historic in stock trading. Within a few days he opened a brokerage office and told bar loungers at the Imperial Hotel that he had inside tips on American markets. The Japanese speculators are just as gullible and greedy as American ones; they grinned and hissed admiringly before this financial wizard; soon, more than six hundred thousand dollars had been entrusted to him, and his cabled investments, thank God, turned out luckily. Thus he won the businessmen's hearts, which are kept in their pocketbooks; willingly they introduced him into the very offices of which the F.B.I. needed sketches and descriptions. Under police escort, they let him see restricted areas in the harbors of Kobe, Yokohama, and Nagasaki. Now the F.B.I. files began to be enriched with confidential data smuggled to America under the most inquisitive noses of Japanese officials.

So trusting were Stanley's Tokyo friendships that he was able to embark on a government ship for Shanghai. Midway in the Yellow Sea, Chinese planes began to drop bombs upon the decks.

"I was scared and I prayed," Stanley later confided to Hoover. "Probably I am the only F.B.I. man who ever prayed for the Japs to win and the Chinese to lose!"

In Shanghai his first job was to investigate an address which, he had learned, was a contact for Japanese and German agents operating in the United States. Stanley knew of it as the "C. S. Wang Travel Service" at 420 Szechuan Road. He now found that the number was actually the office of the China Travel Service, a respectable and innocent institution. In a back room, however, there dozed an elephantine bookkeeper named C. S. Wang; mail addressed to the imaginary travel service promptly reached this spy. Poor, sleepy Wang! He never found out that every night for weeks his desk was searched—not by George Stanley, for no F.B.I. special agent ever has to break the law; he does sometimes cultivate overzealous friends. Information from Wang's pigeonholes spotted for the F.B.I. a string of spies working in the United States; from then on they could tail them, and knew just what they were up to.

In his bland and affable way, Stanley gathered a harvest of facts in Shanghai. His gentle innocence seemed to dispel all suspicion—the very quality the F.B.I. had tried to smash in him was now stocking its files.

Before any suspicion was aroused, he slipped away to new fields, wandering among the booths of money changers in Baghdad, the Nazi book shops in Teheran (where he played dominoes with chiefs of German intelligence), and down the crooked streets of Jerusalem. Once a two-seater plane in which he was flying fell into the sandy midwaste of the Iranian desert. The pilot was killed; Stanley, unscratched, was stranded in the dunes; hidden on his person was half a million dollars in American money. For days he lived on goats' milk and watermelon. Rescued by caravan, he laughed the authorities out of searching him and eventually delivered the money safely to certain persons who needed it for counter-intelligence expenses.

In Syria he was thrown into jail and threatened with the firing squad by officers of Vichy France. Teaching the officers to play poker, he bluffed his way out. Soon he was in the Balkans, where official spying was at its worst. Every night someone went through Stanley's bags. It became a game; he learned to pack his things in a geometrical pattern, the top part of a tobacco pouch pointing west by northwest, the head of a fountain pen, north by northeast, boxing the compass with his effects so that he could tell every time his articles were moved. Yet cunningly concealed among shirts and neckties were confidential reports still to be sent home. Not once were they detected. There was a day when certain suspected travelers were blown to death by bombs planted in their own luggage; Stanley's ever constant checking of his own bags probably saved his life.

Traveling through Bulgaria, his car was stalled in the mud and had to be pulled out by oxen. A Nazi official lent him a plane to fly him on to the capital. In another Balkan country he was under suspicion and constantly followed by Gestapo agents. With a miniature camera in his hip pocket, he photographed his pursuers and sent the prints to the German Ambassador with a vehement protest against such surveillance. The Gestapo agents were fired in disgrace.

Who can fathom the maelstrom of Balkan politics? Yet Stanley plunged into that whirlpool of confusion, got his hands on vital data, and reported them without ever betraying himself. A few hours after France fell, he traveled through the enemy lines, talking French with Frenchmen and German with Germans and sending in the best account we had so far received of the might of the Wehrmacht and the internal reasons for the fall of France.

Hastening on to Munich, he became familiar with habitués of the Brown House and favorite beer halls of German officials.

"More than once," Stanley says, "I had the chance to assassinate Hitler and Goering in their own offices. I wanted to do it—in my heart I believed there was no better way in which I could have served—but my orders were to watch and wait and that is what I had to do."

Friends he made in Berlin took him into private offices of buildings on the Tierpitzufer and Rankestrasse, where the supreme intelligence agencies of the Reich were housed. German businessmen called him "their understanding American friend"; they introduced him to diplomats, boasted of their plans.

In his rôle of financier who liked to do business with Hitler, Stanley was allowed to travel freely back and forth from Berlin to Madrid and Lisbon, in one month alone flying more than sixty-five thousand miles.

He was received in secret Nazi offices in Stockholm and Helsinki. Once, flying high over Nazi-controlled Norway, his ice-covered plane was riddled by German antiaircraft fire and fell three thousand feet out of control before the pilot righted it. A companion plane was shot down in flames. But later the Germans apologized profusely; they hadn't realized who it was!

In Finland he posed as a wealthy lumberman and was

taken by Helsinki financiers on a tour of the great forest of
the Karelian peninsula. That was in the late spring of 1941.
As the train carried him deeper into the woods, he began to
notice thousands of helmets stacked at one station, at another, sleds, and then knapsacks, army blankets, rifles—all
German products piled on the platforms. While he talked
largely to his companions of the paper factory he might
build, his mind was racing far ahead of the train. He had
scented a terrific secret!

Back in Helsinki he delved deeper, learning of the trans-
fer of German troops from Norway to the high Finnish frontier. These troop movements had remained a secret because travel of civilians was forbidden, except to affable
American financiers. Now, too, he understood the recent
concentration of German officers in the Torni and Kamp
Hotels in Helsinki.

Hitler was preparing an immediate surprise attack on
Russia!

Thanks to Stanley, a prediction of German treachery
was on Hoover's desk a month before they sprang. And
here, a curious circumstance. Naturally, the F.B.I. was
closely watching all Germans in Washington; within an
hour after Soviet officials were told what we had learned,
the Ambassador, Constantin Oumansky, rang the doorbell
of the German Embassy. One must wonder why! What
could Oumansky have hoped to gain by confronting the Germans with his new knowledge? Certainly Dr. Hans Thomsen, Chargé d'Affaires for the Reich, could not have been
expected to confess. On the other hand, information that
the Russians were already warned of the coming German
attack would be vital to the German generals. The mystery
grew even darker because, so far as we were ever able to discover, Thomsen sent no report to Berlin on this Oumansky
interview.

Meanwhile, Stanley was traveling back and forth over
the ice-packed Baltic sea, draining information from Finnish and German travelers. Flying from secret airfields in

Finland, he talked with German fighter pilots at Abo and
Königsberg; he watched the embarkation of Nazi troops
at Stralsund for Norway, and sent home constant reports of
the Nazi strength. On June 21 he counted dozens of long
trains carrying troops with light artillery up to the Soviet
border. Then he knew! The attack on Leningrad was only a
matter of hours! His report to that effect actually reached
F.B.I. offices two hours before the onslaught.

Most people would have been tempted to call it a day.
But Stanley went back into Germany. In the next few months
he learned valuable details about Berlin's Director of Espionage in America, Walter Krappe. In Krappe's menage
and everywhere else the Germans still took Stanley for an
American businessman really sympathetic to the Nazi cause.
He crouched with officers and civilians in air-raid shelters
off Friedrichstrasse and Unter den Linden while the RAF
spilled blockbusters on the doomed city. He shared their
perils with them, they shared their secrets with him, and he
kept nothing from the F.B.I.

As 1941 wore on, and all Americans began to be hated
in Berlin, Stanley's food coupons were taken away from
him; he was arrested and given the third degree; the side-
walks of Berlin were too hot for his O'Sullivan heels. The
last item he picked up was the hint of a plan to send out
saboteurs by submarine. That tip, too, reached U. S. officials
in time!

While Stanley could still travel, he flew to South America. Before he got back to Washington he was to visit
every South American country. In one capital he studied
English from a juggler in a vaudeville show who was the
chief Gestapo agent in the area. With his new proficiency,
he then composed a letter to the President of the United
States, signed by a whole group of German sympathizers,
urging Mr. Roosevelt to support the Axis demands. By
indirect means, he got a carbon of the letter to F.B.I.
headquarters; the President was tipped off in advance and
chuckled mightily when he got the letter.

In another South American country Stanley became head of a Communist party school. When a young radical was killed in a riot, Stanley was one of the guards of honor around the coffin. A local newspaper was about to take a picture of the casket sentries but a Communist leader yanked Stanley out of the line, crying:

"You are going to be a most valuable Communist agent! We don't want you to get your picture in the paper so that you can be identified by the ——— ——— F.B.I.!"

As things once more became too hot, Stanley started off from Recife, Brazil, in a two-motor Sikorsky seaplane for Trinidad. Over the Atlantic the plane developed motor trouble and came down on the sea. They drifted through a starless night until Stanley and his pilot heard a plane, their rocket pistols were seen, and they were rescued.

It was then that Hoover suggested Stanley come home for a rest. But by the time he reached Washington, there was a case waiting for him!

Eight German saboteur agents had just landed on the Atlantic coast, by submarine. As you remember, they were promptly nabbed. One carried a handkerchief which, under chemical development, showed in secret writing the name and address of an ex-clergyman living in a slum rooming house in Newark. His name was Carl Emil Ludwig Krepper. Although the F.B.I. were sure that Krepper had been trained in espionage schools in Berlin and Barcelona, they did not know what job Walter Krappe had given him to do. It was up to Stanley to find that out.

At first Krepper proved to be a tough customer, principally because Stanley had been given the wrong password. Once that was rectified, Krepper accepted Stanley as an authentic Reich agent just out of a submarine. But he contemptuously criticized the new arrival's technique.

"The cut of your clothes!" he wailed. "They are too obviously German to fool these Americans!"

"But," sputtered Stanley, "I bought dees suit in New York—in Massy's."

"Don't say 'dees' like dot! Don't say Massy's like dot!" cried the exasperated Krepper. "Your German accent gifs you away. Say Macy's!"

"Macy's," repeated Stanley humbly.

Krepper devoutly believed that Stanley came to him straight from Walter Krappe; he was willing to help destroy United States military installations and build a secret radio transmitter for easier communication with Berlin. He disclosed that his assignment from Krappe was to provide hiding rooms for saboteurs arriving by submarine. These conversations were recorded and sealed Krepper's doom, but until the day of his trial, the spy refused to believe that Stanley had taken him in. When the facts came out in court, he stood up in the courtroom and screamed with rage. Soon he was doing twelve years in Leavenworth.

Stanley came back to Washington, sunny-smiling and eager to go again to the ends of the earth. Instead, he was given a new job—revising the index cards in one of the top-floor files! Why? For one thing, he might well have become too well known to the enemy; for another, he had earned a little scholarly repose and quiet.

Often Hoover is asked how the astounding organization of the German spy system was defeated at every turn in the United States. And why was our counter-intelligence so successful? The German cleverness came to nothing because everything they tried was blueprinted in advance; their agents followed instructions like robots. If things went wrong, and a change of plan was instantly necessary—when resourcefulness and initiative and self-reliance counted—they became confused. Our men were on their own. They were told what we wanted, and we left it to them how to get it! That is a difference that belongs to free men; to democracy!

The Master

WHAT constitutes a master stroke in the fine art of spying is a debatable question.

Prior to the Russo-Japanese War of 1904, a Japanese officer supposedly turned spy and furnished the Russians with vital military plans. He was later caught trying to steal more, and was executed by the Japanese. So the Russians, convinced that the information was bona fide, decided to go on what they had. But the whole thing had been planted. The pretended spy had been working for his own government. His capture, his disgrace, even his death, were the final touches that completely deceived the enemy. A fine stroke, indeed, but hardly the work of a master hand.

During World War II, the British wanted to mislead the Germans about the impending invasion of Sicily. So they created a fictitious British officer with an imaginary past bolstered with letters and pictures of pretended relatives. They obtained a body, put it in uniform, and provided it with fake dispatches telling about coming invasions everywhere—except in Sicily.

They tossed the body overboard off the Spanish coast, where it washed ashore, apparently the victim of an airplane crash. Nazi agents managed to get copies of the documents before the local British consul claimed the body and its belongings. The trick had worked.

199

But still the master touch is lacking, as it was in another highly touted case in World War II which involved a much overrated spy called Cicero, who photographed important documents at the British Embassy in Ankara, Turkey, and sold them to the German Embassy at such fantastic prices that he was called the highest paid spy in history.

Such work requires only the technique of a sneak thief, not that of a mastermind. Moreover, the buyers are usually smart enough to label the purveyor for what he is, as the Germans did in this case. They "took" Cicero with the oldest of rackets, the "green goods game," by paying him off in counterfeit British notes. Far from being the highest paid spy, Cicero ranks as spydom's biggest sucker.

The master touch is in the hidden hand that makes the puppets dance. It is the pitiful victims who indulge in grand heroics. Major John André, who was sent on a spy's mission during the American Revolution, proved so green at the trade that he was shocked when he learned that the Americans intended to hang him instead of shooting him. As if it really mattered.

Yet such niceties persist. In World War I a German officer, caught in disguise behind the American lines, was sentenced to be shot at sunrise, three miles outside of camp. There was no sunrise, but merely a dreary, rainy dawn. As the spy was marched along the muddy road by the plodding firing squad he kept growling angrily:

"What an outrage! This to happen to me. To be treated as common swine. Me, a member of the Kaiser's elite guard. To be marched through the middle of all this rain and muck. Have they no regard for an officer and a gentleman? What insult—what indignity—"

"Aw, shut up!" snapped one of the doughboys. "What are you griping about? Look at us—we've got to march back."

That brings us back to the question of the master spy. The answer is simple, but twofold: Don't get caught if you can help it. If you do, be sure you have a way out.

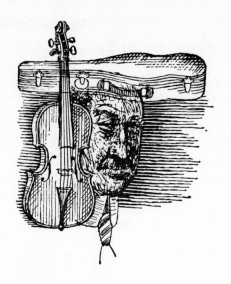

The Master

THOMAS JOHNSON

"IT IS a terrible affair," said the Chief of the French secret service in Switzerland. He spoke almost in a whisper. His working face showed strong emotion.

"What a blow they have dealt us, those Germans!" he exclaimed. "Fooled us about their great offensive that almost crushed first the British Army, then ours. Tricked our secret service like schoolboys. Caught there in Germany twenty-one of our good men, whom we depended on, and *pouf*—snuffed them out. A firing squad at dawn. Then, in those men's names, they sent us forged false reports. We never knew, until too late."

Eyes flashing, he struck the table a blow that made the glasses ring.

"One man did that!" he cried. "One man, though The Master of many more, men and women. Ah, what a Master,

201

of things dark and sinister! He is a veritable Mephistopheles!"

Cautiously the Frenchman looked about the obscure
café, then leaned forward and lowered his voice again.

"And now," he whispered, "that man, that devil, that
Master Spy—he is here!"

The American officer in civilian clothes started, and
looked about too. He was not yet inured to all the game's
abrupt transitions from dull monotony to sudden transfix-
ing flashes of melodrama that proved stark truth. He
smiled apologetically.

"You mean somewhere here in Switzerland, of course,"
he said.

"Right here in Berne," the French chief replied. "Perhaps we pass him on the street and do not know him. Perhaps," waving his hand toward a nondescript group just out
of earshot, "perhaps he sits at that table and watches us.
Who knows? He has two, three, four, one cannot know how
many identities."

Then with a shrug:

"Eh, *bien,* this Mephistopheles is human, for he leaves
trails, and he has not caught all the hounds of our Deuxième Bureau. The trail ends in Berne. He is here, contriv-
ing who knows what new evil to the Allied cause. It is for
us, all of us, to snuff him out in his turn. That is why I asked
you to meet me here—to beseech the help of the American
service."

The American thrilled at the idea.

"You flatter us," he said, "asking us to help catch the
famous Master. We've heard of him, even if we are new at
this 'secret stuff.' The Germans can't have all the crew of
attachés and agents and spies they have in Switzerland without there being some leaks." He grinned. "And do you
know," he said, "the good old American dollar is a regular
divining rod when it comes to finding those leaks."

The Frenchman was beginning to smile, too.

"Yes," he said playfully, "I hope so. Last week our man

in the office of Captain von Bismarck (a schemer, that one, like his famous ancestor) said he was roaring with laughter over some false information they had sold the stupid Yankees."

The American's smile turned to a flush.

"Oh, he was, was he?" he said dryly. "Well, maybe he'll be surprised—he and the rest of them."

Now, the prediction came true. The Americans did catch The Master Spy. How, is one of the most thrilling true tales of our secret service in World War I. A very little appeared then in Swiss newspapers when for a short time the case of The Master was a *cause célèbre*. But that little barely skimmed the surface of the depths of mystery and intrigue, of consummate plotting and consummate evil, that lay beneath.

This is not fiction. The Master lived and moved in his mysterious ways for the cause of the German Empire. He was one of the most formidable figures of that half-world where men and women of strange identity, or none, with motives the highest or the basest, flitted and dodged unstoried and unsung, in the sinister war of the spy, and his enemy, the counterspy.

In that war favorite battlegrounds were the neutral countries bordering on Germany: Holland, Denmark, Switzerland, and foremost of these was Switzerland. Surrounded by Germany, Austria, Italy, and France, great Powers in death struggle, little Switzerland had as much chance of escaping unsmirched as has a child in a white dress making mud pies.

Switzerland was on the line of march of the secret war, a natural base for all sorts of shady operations directed by Germany and Austria on the one hand, by Italy and France on the other. Nor were they the only players in the masked game. To this crossroads of Europe all the nations of the world sent members of their Intelligence Services. Here were suave and smiling diplomats in their element, Army officers trying to hide professional stiffness in civilian clothes, ready to buy the information peddled by "traveling salesmen" whose chief stock in trade it was, after trips into one or another of the surrounding countries, or by railroad employees or customs guards, or hotel servants. Spies and spying everywhere. Normal, peaceful citizens scarcely knew where to turn.

The Alps had become a whispering gallery, the clear free air was tainted with deceit. These thousands of invaders had tainted it perhaps, but some Swiss succumbed. Speaking German, French, and Italian, they could turn an honest penny as spies for one Power or another—or several, sometimes on different sides. There were other pennies to be turned carrying messages, or smuggling over the borders.

Nominally, the Swiss secret police watched everyone impartially, especially the military attachés of all the Powers, Allied or Teutonic, to prevent violations of Swiss neutrality. A connection of a numerous and well-known New York family of Swiss ancestry was assigned to watch the Americans, and probably for a time he chuckled in his sleeve. Some German-Swiss officials helped the Germans fight Allied Intelligence Services that infringed Swiss neutrality less than did the Germans, who once considered invading Switzerland as they had invaded Belgium. High Swiss Army officers were on the Allied suspect list, and there was the affair of the four colonels—which comes later. Strangely, Swiss aid to the Germans helped end the career of a spy-ace—The Master.

Early in 1918, long before the Frenchman and the American met in the Berne café, all the Intelligence Services had but one thought, the great German spring offensive. The Germans sought to conceal their plans, to mislead the Allies, who strove by every means to find out when, where, and how the blow would fall. Fierce and unscrupulous waged the secret war. Switzerland's half-world hummed with the Allied spy drive to get into Germany and secure the precious information.

By land, black closed cars sought hidden byroads near

the frontier. By water, motorboats slipped across Lake Constance to get strong swimmers within reach of the German shore, before patrol boats brought a pistol fight and sudden death in the dark. In the air, supposedly neutral, hum of motors was heard at night, and brave men dropped by parachutes tried the hard task of deceiving grim German spy-hunters, who, too, lived with wits astrain, to repel the stealthy invasion. All the Allies worked together, the splendid British secret service, the Italians, adept at stealth, the enthusiastic if amateur Americans, and most numerous of all, the French. From a score of points in Switzerland, they tried to get their trained men through the Swiss and German net.

At a French vice-consulate in a certain smaller Swiss city, perhaps the regular business that the office did with its right hand concealed and aided what it did with its left. The French were not the only ones thus ambidextrous. Anyway, there were rumors in the half-world.

There came one day to this modest and retiring vice-consulate, a caller who put his foot in the door, then showed a badge that the staff recognized all too well.

"Swiss secret police," they whispered.

To resist meant at least arrest and deportation from Switzerland; to yield might mean a thorough search, producing evidence that would cause far more serious international complications. With quick nervous strides the unwelcome visitor gained the center of the room, a wiry figure of middle height, dominating all. His face, that of a man of about thirty-eight, bespoke determination, magnetism, even dominance: a forehead broad, imposing, over black eyes flashing keenly behind glasses; nose straight as an emperor's; mouth masked by a dark-brown mustache.

"Let no one leave," he said in excellent French. "I am as you see, an officer of the Swiss Government. I have come to look for suspected violation of Swiss neutrality."

Then dramatically he thrust forward a pointing hand.

"Let me see the contents of that safe!" he said.

"But, Monsieur," an official remonstrated, "this is a French vice-consulate. I assure you, there is nothing wrong here—and we have never been asked to open our safe."

"Nevertheless," said the visitor, "I demand that you do so."

The Frenchman shrugged his shoulders. The really dangerous things, he hoped, were not in the safe. He stood by while the man with the badge eagerly transferred papers and memorandum books to a small bag he carried.

"I shall examine these," he said, "at my leisure."

The Frenchman stepped forward.

"Examine them here if you must," he cried, "but you have no right to take them away."

Like a flash the visitor's hand went to his coat pocket.

"Ah, have I not?" There was a ring of command in his voice. "We shall see. Let no one move."

Nimbly he stepped to and through the door, slammed it and shot the bolt. Came the sudden drumming of a powerful motor.

The secret war in Switzerland began to go badly for the Allies. In another Swiss city, a prosperous Swiss merchant, perhaps a trifle pro-Ally, received a call from a Swiss secret police agent who insisted on seeing reports of his traveling men in Germany. The Swiss agent showed a badge. A masterful man—yes: middle height, wiry, not quite forty, mustache, glasses, piercing black eyes.

"It is the same man," said the French secret service.

Next day came a code telegram from Zurich. The identical Swiss agent had called there upon a trusted Allied agent, shown the badge, and asked questions that could be asked only by someone who had seen papers that might have been in the vice-consulate safe. He seemed to be on a trail or two.

"It becomes serious," said the French. "What are the Swiss up to?—Or is it, after all, the Swiss? But that badge——"

There are French Swiss as well as German, and one of these reported next day:

"A high police official of Zurich says this man is a bona fide Swiss agent."

The Zurich official was a German Swiss, and had been long on the Allied suspect list. They could prove nothing, but they could watch. Then came a report from Geneva:

"The British aviator X——, here on leave, has been seen much with a man about whom we have been curious for some time. He passes as of the Swiss secret police, and speaks English well. He seems not quite forty, middle height, slim but strong, brown mustache, glasses, black eyes very keen and glittering."

Then like a thunderclap, word from the Deuxième Bureau in Paris:

"The British Independent Air Force who conduct from airdromes in the American area in Lorraine night bombing raids upon the German Rhine cities, believe that the secret of their system of signaling by lights at night has been betrayed to the Germans. Several times lately German airplanes have flown at night over British airdromes, flashing British code signals to light up. When that was done, the Germans bombed and machine-gunned the airdromes, destroying airplanes and killing and wounding aviators and mechanics. There is reason to believe they got this information in Switzerland."

Search as they would, the British could find nowhere in the Royal Air Force an aviator named X——.

But there was worse to come. All this time, the French secret service in Switzerland had been congratulating itself on its success in getting men into Germany, and their reports out again. The great German spring offensive of 1918, these reports said, would be a stupendous blow against the French in the Champagne, possibly linked with a pincer attack on the new and small American force near Toul. So while other channels of information contradicted, steps were taken to be ready. On March twenty-first the great blow fell—not at all on the French in Champagne or the Americans in Lorraine, but on the British on the Somme, a hundred miles and more away. The French could hardly believe this was the main attack, and their reinforcements were slow, all but too slow, to aid the hard-pressed British. Then suddenly the French spy reports from Germany became queerly mixed.

Expert checking showed them a combination of truth and falsehood so ingenious that it was almost impossible to tell which was which. Much of the true information the Allies already had—and the Deuxième Bureau found that the Germans must have known it. Horror-struck, they tested out their supposedly safe and sure information service working from within Germany via Switzerland. They ordered it to secure plans of the plant of the Badische Anilin Fabrik at Ludwigshafen, the great German gas factory—of which they had already plans they knew were accurate. By the underground railway, bearing the proper marks of the French secret service, came back a set of plans labeled "Badische Anilin Fabrik"—but they were not the true plans. The Germans had been tricking the French secret service.

How? For how long? Here was a task worthy the keen Latin mind, to be done in desperate haste, for other German drives were coming, even now were in preparation. Where? When? Not only had a trusted source of information dried up, it had been polluted by the enemy. And the trained agents who had crossed the German border so confidently but who seemed to have sent back false reports—where were they?

Like eager hounds the Deuxième Bureau beat the cover of Switzerland and the German border, and soon found a scent here, a trail there, small bits that, put together, revealed the dim outlines of tragedy. Every one of the twenty-one skilled agents who had gone into Germany to find out about the great drive had been doomed before he crossed the frontier. The Germans had let them walk into the parlor, locked the door, watched from behind a curtain while they went about getting information, noted every move. With greatest pains they had found out how the French spies sent back their reports, by secret messengers, code telegrams, newspaper advertisements, whatever means. Then the Germans had pounced. One French spy after another had stood gray-faced before a gray-clad firing squad. One by one the Germans had snuffed them out—and sent back in their names falsified reports. It was indeed for the French a terrible affair. And how many British lives had it cost?

French secret service sought the creator of this masterpiece of trickery, this work of art in strangling, misty gray with its gobbet of crimson. Certainly there appeared the figure of The Master. But only gradually. For long he was a name, a phantom, and not even those who had seen him, like the staff of the vice-consulate, knew just who or what he was. They cursed him as The Master—and then looked over their shoulders.

The French secret service Chief continued:

"Every vice-consulate man we set looking for him, all over Switzerland. And *voilà!* Right here in Berne one comes to me greatly moved.

" 'I have found him!' he cries. 'In the office of the police!'

"I assure you, I could hardly control myself.

" 'But certainly,' says my man. 'From the hall I saw him talking, laughing with a high police officer. A typist told me he was a good friend of the officer and comes often. He left, he took a taxicab, he walked around a block, then to an apartment house and into a door on the first floor. The *concierge* was a veritable Prussian *Unteroffizier.* No use to ask him. But the *concierge* came out, walked up the street. I seized some newspapers from an ancient *vendeuse,* I ran in, rang his doorbell. There came to the door a man of the height of him whom I followed, but broader, darker, with heavier features, different expression, in short, another man —and in the uniform of a captain in the Germany Army. I looked into the apartment, a small one; and I swear there was nobody else. The man I had seen go in—was not there.'

" 'I had just wits enough to offer a newspaper. The German officer looked hard at me, took the paper, fumbled in his pocket, went back into the apartment and took from an overcoat some money—and again, I swear, the overcoat was that of the man I had followed, the man of the vice-consulate. But this captain was another man, or seemed so.'

"You know, my friend," the French Chief continued, "we have a little what you call Rogues' Gallery, with pictures of those who are suspect. Almost immediately our man chose a picture. 'Here he is!' he said. It was a Captain von Einem, who voyaged often by government permission between Germany and Switzerland, to care for German soldiers interned here. For long we had suspected that under cover of this humane work he was part of their underground railway, a messenger for and probably a recruiter of spies. I ordered him watched day and night, and soon our agent reported:

" 'This morning Captain von Einem took the train for Zurich. I followed, and at the station a limousine met him. He closed the curtains. The car drove slowly for a half-hour, then to an apartment house in a quiet street. The door opened, and out stepped—another man. The Captain had vanished. This new man wore rather sportive civilian clothes, was short, stooping. I caught a glimpse of his face —not that of Captain von Einem. Into the house went my man. Around the corner I bought a basket of vegetables, turned up my coat collar and went back. The *concierge* was surely German, but a woman was sweeping and to her I said:

" ' "These are ordered by Herr Glauber, who just alighted from the automobile."

" ' "Get away!" she cried to me. "We know no Herr Glauber here. That was Herr Michaelsen, who has lived here this long time. You have the wrong house."

" 'And they told me at our Zurich branch:

" ' "Yes, Michaelsen is on our suspect list. He is attached to the German vice-consulate, in the bureau for exchanging German coal for Swiss milk, cheese, and other products. He speaks German, French, English, and German-Swiss. That would make him a dangerous spy if he were discreet enough. But he lives a dissolute life, drinking and women. Every dive-keeper in Zurich must know him. But this Captain von Einem, we never heard of his being in Zurich." ' "

The French Chief leaned back and lighted a cigarette.

"What an affair, my friend," he said, with an expressive gesture. "Was the raider of the vice-consulate, with his Swiss badge, friend of the police of Berne and Zurich, also Captain von Einem of Berne, and again Herr Michaelsen of Zurich? Which was his real identity? And all this elaborate deceit by a Swiss agent merely seeking neutrality violations? He could be only one thing, a consummately clever German agent, a Master Spy.

"Since the Germans had snuffed out our twenty-one agents our other eyes and ears had been the more vigilant. Already we had heard about The Master—as they called him here in Switzerland. To Michaelsen we owed the idea to search the underworld dives. I have called him master of things dark and sinister, a Mephistopheles. Listen:

"He had some unholy power over many of the professional spies and informers of the Swiss underworld; those who will do anything for a price; report what indiscreet Allied officers a little 'zigzag' might reveal, crack a safe, steal, beat up, drug or kill an Allied agent, for enough money. Some he held by bribes, some by threat of exposure, some wretches did his bidding for the drugs he always had.

"His power went beyond the underworld. The two Swiss police officers are only the beginning. We cross his slimy trail everywhere. We find him or Von Einem or Michaelsen in touch with highest and lowest. In the same day he talks with Walter Rathenau, head of the commercial staff at the German Legation which we have long suspected did legitimate business through the front door and secret service through the back, then with a bank teller accused of theft who then gets a first-class Swiss lawyer and provides high bail."

"We have heard something of it," the American said. "The man follows in Stieber's footsteps."

"In Stieber's crooked footsteps!" the Frenchman exclaimed. "That degenerate founder of the Prussian secret service used every base means to force men to work for him. Here in Switzerland this Master builds an edifice like Stieber's Green House in Berlin, where through the lowest desires, through lust, and avarice, then through threat and blackmail, he bends all to his purpose.

"Wherever he goes, this Master finds victims. There is more than one crooked bank teller in his power. Perhaps he first tempted this one to speculate, then caused his arrest by The Master's friend, the police official. In many a Swiss bank that handles Allied money he has agents who tell him how it is spent. He has bribed Swiss railroad conductors, hotel chambermaids, telegraph employees. How do the Germans know so well what happens at the border? Customs inspectors! Always he and his agents seek out the morally weak—to corrupt them, make them weaker. Be a spy for me, he says, or I will betray you to the Swiss police. Then to his police friends he gives underworld information in trade for what they know about our Allied secret services here. Perhaps even some of our men are *'agents doubles,'* in his pay. He has plenty of money.

"A Mephistopheles!" the Frenchman exclaimed, with despairing rage. "He harms us more than half their German generals. He steals the British signals, and destroys more airplanes than Richthofen. Every day many French and British and Italian and American soldiers die because of him. It is the affair of all of us."

That affair, which the French Chief had called terrible, might have been unsolved but for events that had happened in Germany before the World War began or was even dreamed of by normal, happy people. Then a family of such people, *wohlgeboren,* of position and means, lived in a picturesque city of the romantic Rhineland. They had peace and comfort, busy days, and happy evenings after the sun had set on vineclad slopes: father and mother; the daughter, Margrete, blue-eyed and fair, always laughing; two boys, one to be sure rather slender but bright and cheerful, the other straight-backed, ruddy, proud of his uniform of officer in a crack German regiment. How happy they were, they and their American friend and guest, when the young officer was ordered to join the Kaiser's personal staff.

"I feel as I felt in 1870 when I won my Iron Cross," said his old soldier father, as they bade farewell to the new aide-de-camp of their Emperor.

"It is a great honor," he confided to the American. "Our Kaiser is strict with his personal staff, but what an opportunity!"

A few days later the American had to leave reluctantly, to say good-by to Margrete with her songs and laughter, standing arm in arm with the other brother, who must find a career less arduous than the Army. They had corresponded, then suddenly, the letters from Germany had stopped coming. Then the war, and though the American had wondered often, he had heard no more. When the United States entered the war, the American, like many who knew Germany, had been assigned to secret service work in Switzerland. And now he had been asked to help hunt The Master.

On this task he concentrated eagerly, studying papers in The Master's dossiers in French or American files, cudgeling his brains day and night, seeking odd haunts, watching every face. And so, because he courted Lady Luck, she smiled on him. One day, out of the procession of faces in streets, cafés, theaters, he caught a familiar one. It was the face of the slight, home-keeping younger brother of the peaceful Rhineland days. But how changed!

The face was emaciated; the eyes were staring from haggard, putty-colored cheeks. The body, slighter than ever,

was bent a little as if under a weight. He seemed a man possessed by overmastering forces. The American was
shocked. A rush of old memories made him follow the German, who was in dark civil garb, down a side-street, to slap
him on the back and cry his name in German.

Startled, the man turned, then grasped the American's
hand with both of his.

"We are still good friends," he said. "Your Wilson has
said it is only the governments that fight. We are not
enemies."

They talked for a few minutes, the German seeming always tense, controlling himself with difficulty. No wonder
that his appearance had shocked the American. He told
that he had been discharged from the Army as consump-
tive. Then he reverted to President Wilson, the American
part in the war. Was it true that the Americans were really
fighting to dethrone the Hohenzollerns, help Germany free
herself? Again and again, he asked about that with fanatical earnestness almost gruesome. Coughing terribly, he
seemed a figure of doom.

"This man," thought the American, "has something on
his mind, and it's nearly killing him." And aloud: "What
are you doing in Switzerland?"

The German's face contorted painfully.

"I am doing—government work," he said at last, "work
that I hate."

"Government work—that I hate." The words leaped into fire before the American's eyes. What had he learned in
the secret war? "Distrust everybody. Secret service knows
three powerful motives: patriotism, hatred, greed. Use
them." But how? Which was the key to his friend's secret?
Calmly and deliberately, the American decided to use all
the craft, tact, resource he had to probe the German's mind.

"It is not a nice thing," he said, ten years later in his
quiet American home, "to wheedle and goad an old friend
into telling his inmost thoughts. But war is war. No one who
does not know now, must ever know who that man was."

Then, on promise that the German should be called, as

the American secret service really called him, "Zero," the American retold his horrible story. He had heard it first, there in Berne, after hours of talk, in which Zero had refused with what seemed fearful reluctance to mention "the good days before the war." Suddenly he gave in completely.

"I can hold it back no longer," he said, words tumbling out. "It is more than my disease that has changed me so. It is grief, and hatred. Though I am a German, *wohlgeboren,* yet I hate the German Empire as it is today. I hate the Hohenzollerns. I hate the Army officers. Listen!

"You have talked about those happy days when you visited us in the Rhineland. You remember our dear father and mother, and Margrete, and how our brother went to join the Kaiser's staff, and how glad we all were and went down to the station to see him off? That was the last happy day of my life, I think. Soon after my brother left us an attempt was made to assassinate the Kaiser, one of several. Nerves shaken, the Kaiser withdrew to a secluded hunting lodge, taking a few trusted officers, including my brother.

"The Kaiser slept in an inside bedroom, protected by an anteroom, where all night two officers took turns sleeping and standing guard. As dawn broke, my brother lighted a cigarette, relaxed and unbuttoned his tunic. At that instant the Kaiser stepped into the room.

"Embarrassed, because the Kaiser was such a stickler, my brother jumped to his feet, clicked his heels, and in an evil moment thrust his hand toward his tunic to button it. But sudden fear of another attempt to kill him seized the Kaiser. Like a flash, he drew a revolver and shot my brother dead.

"An instant later, he realized what he had done and almost collapsed. He tried to make every amend. It was called a hunting accident, and a brother officer brought home the body. We were heartbroken, but so thankful to that officer. A handsome fellow he was, a typical Prussian officer. Ah, that devil—I wish I had my hands on his throat."

Zero's emotion, stronger, almost overpowered him.

"You have spoken of Margrete, my sister, how she sang and laughed. Your heart would break to see her now. He took her, then threw her off. *Ach, meine Schwesterchen!*"

A paroxysm of coughing came, mingled with sobs.

"After caring for her, I started to find him, and just then came the war. The Empire dealt us blow after blow. Mother died of grief and shock. Father has not been the same, but they made me leave him and go into the Army. You know I was never strong, and it all broke my health. They sent me here to Switzerland, but to do their dirty work, to be a spy, slave of a man who typifies everything I most detest. Now I have told you."

One emotion after another the American had felt, grief, anger, sympathy, but always he had remembered the game that duty, love of country, made him play. Now the back of his neck began to tingle. He half arose from his seat.

"Who is this man?" he asked.

Zero looked up wearily.

"They call him The Master," he replied.

"The Master?" the American's voice thrilled. "Why, my old friend, God himself has given you this chance for revenge. Every Allied secret service in Switzerland wants the information you can reveal. It will hit the German Empire that you have reason to hate, harder than a lost battle."

That began a struggle, fought out by the German against himself. Should he forget the habits of a lifetime and betray this detested servant of a detested ruler and government? Repeatedly the American assured him that would help bring to Germany the democracy for which the Americans were fighting. He used every argument he could think of, the invasion of Belgium, the *Lusitania,* other acts of the Imperial German Government.

"All the world fights against that government," he cried. "Why shouldn't you? It has fought you, killed your brother and your mother, ruined your sister, wrecked your health. If you don't take this chance, it will be on your soul until you die."

Finally, he won.

"God help me, I'll do it," Zero whispered, and he began to tell what he knew about The Master. He could tell more than almost anyone in Switzerland, but not all at once. Fear would seize him, or some vestige of loyalty to the Fatherland of before the war. The American trembled lest The Master's figure, just assuming tangible shape, should melt away before flesh and blood could be caught surely. Conferring with the chiefs, French and American, searching records, he shaped a cross-examination of Zero as comprehensive as it was hazardous. Now that he knew Zero's connection with the German secret service, he knew they could not be seen together. So each meeting must be in a different place, always one well hidden. The more securely concealed, the more Zero would tell. Danger was constant, and the American carried to these trysts revolver and blackjack. Always in the back of his mind was the thought, "Suppose he is leading me on, after all."

But such of Zero's information as could be checked, proved true. Then at a night meeting in a forest on the outskirts of Berne, the American pressed the German to "come clean," and Zero promised.

"Tomorrow morning," he said, "take the early train for Zurich. The last compartment of the last first-class carriage. Come alone."

The American came alone, but even then as with one hand he opened the door of the last first-class compartment, with the other hand he held in his pocket a Colt automatic. There might still be a trap. At first he saw nobody in the darkened compartment, then a hoarse voice whispered, "Take this." Zero, paler than ever in the half-light, crouched in a corner. He pushed a violin case into the American's hands.

"It's all there," he gasped, "inside the violin. Put on these"—he handed the American a long flowing tie, and a big-brimmed black hat—"and get off at the next station."

Zero scrambled out, and the train started.

A few hours later the American and his chief brought strange notes from the violin, notes written upon the thin

paper used for spy reports. Time after time they had wondered: "But who really is The Master?" Here at last was
the answer. His full stature stood revealed.

He was a man of mark, of influence and power in Germany before the war. Born in Bavaria, in 1880, he had been
educated as an electrical engineer. Social success had been
added to professional, for not only had he been born to excellent position, he was widely cultured, knew seven languages. He was especially charming to women, made
many conquests and had a rather romantic air, enhanced
by skill at amateur theatricals that had taught him makeup
and disguise. War in 1914 found him a councilor of a large
city. As officer on the Western Front he won the Iron Cross.
Wounded, they told him:

"You can do bigger things in secret service."

His dramatic sense influenced the decision, then helped
him create and sustain his three personalities as he spread
his nets in Switzerland. Attached to the commercial staff of
the German Legation at Berne, he strove to outwit the re-
strictions of the Swiss Government, under Allied pressure,
upon trade with blockaded Germany. Introduced to powerful pro-German Swiss business men and bankers, having
ample funds, he engineered daring deals. He evaded the
Swiss regulation that no cotton goods could be exported to
Germany by shipping three thousands of cotton nightshirts
of Falstaffian proportions, eight feet long, balloon-sleeved,
with a few stitches of embroidery. "Embroidered goods"
could go. Rubber he sent labeled "glue." Ruses failing, his
bribed Swiss customs officials passed contraband. To conceal his smuggling, he set up a brokerage office, imported
to Switzerland two million francs' worth of merchandise a
month—which crossed into Germany. As dummy head of
this office he installed the sickly Zero, who seemed an easy
tool, and had been a broker.

Unavoidably he had let Zero see how he not only supplied the Fatherland illegally—despite a blockade he and
most Germans considered cruelly illegal—but made him-

self super-spy super-counterspy, spinning a web that en-
meshed hundreds, thousands of others.

As spy, he or others for him conducted a little school in
Berne, where education was sometimes compulsory. Some
pupils were Alsatians or Lorrainers from among the interned Germans whom Captain von Einem visited; some
underworld characters, accomplished crooks recruited by
Herr Michaelsen; some Swiss, bribed, blackmailed, threatened by The Master. Some were loyal patriotic Germans
who did the work willingly. All were taught how to get into
France, parts to play when they got there, what information to seek, how to report it. So well were they trained and
paid that all too many returned safely.

As counter-spy, The Master loved to undermine the Allied Intelligence. The twenty-one Frenchmen caught and
snuffed out just before the German spring offensive may
have been his greatest single stroke, that won him the valued German decoration of the *Ordre pour le Merite*. But
two hundred, not twenty-one, was the total of his victims.
Two hundred Allied agents had stumbled into The Master's
web, which caught them like barbed wire hidden in high
grass. What he could not find out through his own secret
service, or from his friends in the Swiss police, he got from
a traitor.

As the French Chief had feared, there was in the French
secret service an *"agent double,"* who had worked first in
Switzerland, then in France. He had sold out to The Master,
and he more than any other had been responsible for the
twenty-one being tracked down and shot. It was not long
before, thanks to the Americans, this man faced a firing
squad in the blue uniforms of the French Republic he had
betrayed. His name was Leon Sutor.

To mask his work, The Master had taken every pain,
aided by his Swiss police friends. They told him whom they
suspected as Allied agents, and when he gave them con-
firmatory evidence they kept him out of it. He appeared
openly only twice, at the Brestline and Margeot trials, then

only in one of his identities, without revealing The Master
Spy.

But the hand of The Master slipped twice. He did not
fathom Zero, and in the character of Michaelsen he permitted himself debauchery that could not but react. There
were not alone the apartments in Berne and in Zurich, there
was a secluded villa at Arbon, across Lake Constance from
Germany. A convenient spot for The Master's affairs with
women, and from which to communicate with Germany.
It was guarded carefully. A swift motorboat was always
ready.

That was the tale the notes from Zero's violin told to the
two American secret service officers in Berne that day in
1918. Not an incredible tale to them, who knew the laby-
rinth of intrigue in Switzerland, and could check by other
information The Master's part in it.

"We've got him," said the American Chief. "This clinches
the thing. It's what the French have longed for. We'll give
it to them——

"If our American service gets the credit openly," he explained, as the younger man looked disappointed, "we lose
our greatest advantage in this game. Now they all think we
don't know anything. Let the French appear in it—and no
rough stuff. There's enough here to put him behind bars in
Switzerland for years."

The Chief rubbed his hands cheerfully.

"Guess we've done a little Master Spying ourselves," he
chuckled.

So triumphantly the French Chief showed to someone
higher than any police officer his proofs of The Master's
violation of Swiss neutrality. The Swiss officials were
amazed. This man was an important person, a friend of
many prominent Swiss. Still Swiss police went to the Berne
apartment, where French agents had been on guard against
a tip-off. The knock at the door was unanswered. They
burst it open and stood for a moment aghast. They saw a
man of hideous visage. His face seemed lopsided, one side

swollen, one part a bronzed, healthy color, the other a deadly white. He lacked an eyebrow. His hair stood up crazily askew—a wig! They had caught The Master becoming Von Einem!

Books and papers in the apartment and in Zurich bore out Zero's charges, indicated still greater flights of The Master's genius. After the first Russian revolution of early 1917, the German secret service had taken Lenin from exile in Switzerland through Germany to Russia, on his promise when he had seized power, to dissolve the Russian Army which still faced the Germans, and make peace with them. Some men prominent in Allied countries had begged that Lenin and other Bolsheviks with him be assassinated. But they had gone safely, in their "sealed train," with what result the world knows. There seemed to the Americans some evidence that the hand at the throttle of that train had been The Master's. Proof of that would be highly valuable as information, and propaganda in the highly sensitive Europe of 1918. It might even influence events in Russia. Was there such proof? This question the Americans asked Zero by devious ways.

"In the enclosure of the Lake Constance villa," he replied, "is an outbuilding covering a cesspool. In a suitcase hanging on a peg under the ledge, he kept very important papers. Look there, at once."

That night a burly German on guard at the villa heard an automobile. He hurried out the back gate, and found two men tinkering with a broken-down car. They looked like workmen, wore overalls, spoke German. They were young, good fellows, asked his advice, smoked, passed a bottle as they tinkered. As he realized he had stayed long, and rose to go, he met two more men, bearded faces shielded by broad-brimmed hats, coming from the direction of his gate.

"What do you want here?" he snapped suspiciously.

But the two newcomers were good fellows, too. They had a bottle of their own, and one trolled in fluent German-

Swiss a well-known drinking song. They got into the car, and it drove away. The German stumbled back to his gate.

"Donnerwetter!" he exclaimed. "The light is out!"

In the automobile the two repair men asked eagerly: "Well, what happened? Did you find it?"

"Wait'll I get rid of these whiskers so I can talk," said the singer of drinking songs. "When Fritz came out of the gate, we shinned the wall, but right over the entrance to the outbuilding was a bright electric light. That was ticklish. The air pistol was noiseless, all right, but I hadn't practised enough with it. Finally I hit the light and Alec had the gas masks and rope ladder and grappling hook, and in we went. We didn't quite need the gas masks—almost, though—whew!—before we found the peg. Just then—I was stooping over, giving Alec a hand—a big watchdog attacked my unprotected rear. I almost let Alec slip into the cesspool, but I managed to plug the dog with the air pistol and he went off yelling. A light flashed in the house. So we came away. The suitcase wasn't on the peg—or anywhere else."

That suitcase never was found, for, secretly as he had moved, a few others of The Master's satellites besides Zero knew something of his methods. They were frantically covering his trail. Powerful friends, Germans and Swiss, went to work with equal alacrity—Germans to save a Master Spy, Swiss lest the story of his relations with their police come out. The scandal would have rivaled the famous case of the four colonels. So The Master had one of the best Swiss lawyers, who discovered that confinement, his old wound, and the humiliation of false accusations had weakened The Master physically and mentally. He was transferred from prison to a private asylum near Zurich, where his condition was pronounced not serious enough for strict confinement. He had some visitors.

One evening as he and an attendant amused themselves in the billiard room, gongs rang. There was a cry of "Fire! Fire!" and scurrying feet. The attendant ran out—but first he opened the window. To that window the patient leaped, seized the rope dangling there, lowered himself to the court-yard and ran to a corner of the surrounding wall. He tossed over a handful of pebbles, and the top rungs of a ladder appeared. He was up and over like a flash, to jump into the tonneau of a waiting automobile that started instantly—an automobile of the German Legation. To Lake Constance it sped, to Arbon, where the motorboat was waiting.

Next morning the Chief of the American secret service found on his desk an intercepted telegram from Friedrichshafen in Germany, to the German Legation in Berne. In code it said: "Arrived here safely last night."

With The Master out of Switzerland, his service broke up. Most of its wheels ceased turning in Berne and Zurich. Few others had known any of its ramifications, not even Zero had known all. But he had known more than others. Infuriated at such a blow, the Germans sought an informer, at least a scapegoat, and fixed upon him. They had the Swiss arrest him for a minor passport violation.

Feeling cold fingers close around his own throat, in an agony of fear and physical weakness, he sent word to his sister, Margrete, to avenge whom he had got into this situation. Hoping that through her they could get proofs of her brother's guilt, the Germans let her come. At a heartbreaking meeting in the Berne prison Zero begged her, "Go to the American. He is our only hope."

She went, and would have bravely told again the story of what had happened to her, but this old friend of happier days gently stopped her.

"You needn't tell me that," he said. "Your brother has helped our cause, and I will help him."

He was breaking one of the ironclad rules of secret service:

"Never acknowledge a spy or an informer who has served you and been caught. Even though you have paid him secretly, deny it, disown him."

Zero had neither asked nor received a cent. But to the

young American other rules seemed to apply, too—the rules of humanity, of friendship, of chivalry, even of common sense, for suppose Zero, despairing, revealed the American part in the affair? He sent away a Margrete weeping tears of joy.

Good Swiss lawyers took fees in dollars as well as marks, and in a few days Zero was out of prison, but not safe. His belongings had been ransacked. Wherever he went he was followed. At any moment a knife might be thrust between his ribs. In frightful anxiety, more haggard than ever, he sent word by his sister again:

"For God's sake, get me out of Switzerland."

For some days and nights, Zero and his sister kept in hiding, guarded by an armed member of the American secret service. Then by night their friend took the devoted pair to the Italian border, and left them, in full belief that they were safe at last from the Empire that they hated and had helped to ruin. From that day to this, no word has come from them. Did the German secret service reach out and strike them even in Italy? Did his dread disease claim Zero? Their American friends who tried to save them hope not—but they do not know.

The defeat of The Master is the war exploit of which they are proudest. It won for both decorations. The principal actor, Zero's friend, whom the French Chief begged for aid, who sang the drinking song on the moonlit road by Lake Constance, received another token of which he was proud, a large photograph, autographed "John J. Pershing."

The Master, when last heard of, had resumed his prewar identity and was director of the electrical and engineering works of one of the largest cities in the thriving German Republic.

The Cryptographers' War

LATIN students who trudged through Caesar's Gallic Wars will be pleased to learn that he frequently made his regular military correspondence harder by putting it in cipher, so that people of his own time suffered too. Yet, though Caesar may have impressed his fellow Romans, his artful devices were old hat long before he traded in his battered helmet for a shiny laurel wreath.

Two methods of coding were used in Caesar's time. One was the transposition cipher, wherein the letters of a message were shifted to some other order. The other was substitution, in which the regular letters were replaced by different letters or symbols.

Caesar's system involved elements of both, for he simply pushed each letter four places along, so that the word CIPHER became GMTLIV. This made it easy for the receiver to read, provided he knew the order of the alphabet, which seems to have been a familiar thing in Ancient Rome, though some of our modern reading systems have ignored it.

There followed two-step ciphers, double transpositions and other complex offshoots, but they were still essentially the same by Napoleon's day. Then they began to backslide, because Napoleon moved so fast that he often didn't have time to code his dispatches, and when he did, his codes were so stylized that they were quite easily cracked.

In Civil War days, matters became both better and worse. The Union code makers managed to switch codes and trick them up so handily that Confederate cryptographers were unable to decipher them. They frequently published captured Union dispatches in the newspapers, hoping that loyal Southern readers would help them. The Southerners goofed badly with their own codes, especially when incompetent telegraphers botched them.

All during the nineteenth century, the public was so simple-minded about codes that Poe's story, *The Gold Bug,* which delved into the frequency of letters as a clue to a simple substitution cipher, was acclaimed as something quite wonderful. And Conan Doyle was given the accolade for his story of *The Dancing Men,* wherein the mighty mind of Sherlock Holmes divined that a row of little matchstick figures represented letters of the alphabet.

Either of these examples would be easy picking for modern fans who tackle daily newspaper cryptograms. But over the years, professional cryptographers were by no means idle, either. They devised ciphers based on keywords named after the various inventors—Vigenere, Gronsfeld, Beaufort, and Playfair. Dictionary codes, slide rules, cipher wheels, and other devices came into vogue, systems which created "black chambers" where secret messages were analyzed.

Codes were stolen, treacherously sold, quietly cracked, and filed away for reference when needed. Fake codes were unloaded on unsuspecting buyers. What happened to codes and ciphers is a story in itself.

The Cryptographers' War

FLETCHER PRATT

MORE than any other in history the war that began in 1914 was a cryptographers' conflict. From the day in August of 1914 when German-controlled radio stations all over the world flashed out the message *A SON IS BORN,* codephrase for "War," no great event but was preceded by feverish activity in the code-rooms of the nations; and in many cases victory or defeat was underwritten in those code-rooms before it took place on the battlefield or across the seas.

As the German armies marched to the Marne in the first days of the war, their communications section was faced with totally unexpected difficulties. Von Kluck and von Bülow, commanding the two armies out on the right wing of the wide sweep through Belgium, soon found themselves beyond the reach of personal communication with the main

Army headquarters at Coblenz, moving too fast for messengers to come and go, and with all wires down in their rear. They had to use radio to reach both the high command and each other; had to use it even in communicating with the corps and divisional headquarters under their orders.

When radio was used, the weakness of their cipher system became apparent. Two-step ciphers, the substitution-transposition systems they were using, are quite good when messages can be clearly written out, not quite so good when they must be sent by some form of telegraphy, with the possibilities this entails of confusing one letter with another, and definitely bad under the actual conditions of this war. The air was filled with radio traffic, French, British, Belgian, German, often with several instruments working the same wave-length, jamming one another. Whole sections of messages became lost or unintelligible, and the loss of even one letter in a two-step message which involves double substitution as one of the steps, renders the whole message gibberish. Everything had to be repeated, up to five, ten, or a dozen times, and even then some of the most important communications failed to get through, so the whole of the German march through North France became a chronicle of missed opportunities and faulty cooperation.

At Mons the II and IV German Reserve Corps did not get their orders in time to make a movement von Kluck had astutely planned and the British escaped a trap that had been set for them without being crushed. At Guise, six days later, von Kluck failed to understand orders that came through for him and the French 5th Army slipped from another trap; and meanwhile the French cryptographers, headed by Colonel Givièrge, General Cartier, and Dr. Locard, the famous criminologist, had broken down the German ciphers.

Thus it came about that on the night of September 2, 1914, von Kluck was sent by radio a dispatch from the German high command, which ordered him to close up on von

Bülow to his left, and to press the French southeast away
from Paris. He never received the message but the French
did and understood it. Next morning von Kluck radioed his
headquarters that he was carrying out the plan of campaign
given him when the march through France began—to cross
the Marne and swing southwestward against the city. German headquarters did not get that message for another
thirty-six hours and only after numerous repetitions, and
again the French radios intercepted it and the French de-
cipherers worked out its meaning.

With the messages laid side by side Joffre could see there
would be a wide gap between von Kluck's army, moving
according to the original plan, and von Bülow's next left,
moving southeast according to the new orders. Scouting
and aerial observation confirmed the fact; and out of it
grew the battle of the Marne. A French army poured from
the gates of Paris and clutched von Kluck so close in frontal
battle he could not rectify his error when his message tardily
reached German headquarters and theirs came to him. Another held von Bülow, while into the gap between the two
poured the British with still another French army on their
heels, and the Germans did not win their war that fall.

In the east, the Russians, experts of intrigue, knew well
before the war started that the Germans had, or would have,
their ciphers, but blandly used them right down to the declaration of hostilities as though they suspected nothing.
They had worked out a clever plan: several years before the
war, their experts had prepared a new and very secret cipher that was partly a code. Only one copy was made, and
that locked away in a safe in St. Petersburg. On the day of
the declaration this new cipher was taken from its hiding
place and turned over to General Jilinsky, the Army's high
commander, who sent down orders that copies of the old
cipher were to be destroyed.

The Russian war plan called for the invasion of the East
Prussian province where it juts like a horn over what was
then Russian Poland, by two armies. The First, under Gen-

eral Rennenkampf, was to march in from the east; the Second, commanded by General Samsonov, was to come up from the south, but the two were separated by the forty-mile gap of the region of the Masurian Lakes, a region wild as the Yukon, without railroads, roads, or telegraph lines. The two armies could communicate with each other only by field radio, but the Russian field radio service with those two armies was excellent, for they were the flower of the Tsar's troops, almost the only good troops the Russian Army had, fully trained and fully equipped. They drove in the German outposts and began the advance.

It has been said that General Jilinsky chose this occasion to go on a series of superlative champagne parties, but the story comes from the Bolsheviks, tremendously anxious to discredit everyone in the old regime, and is possibly not true. The only thing certain is that Jilinsky gave the single copy of the new secret field cipher to Rennenkampf of the First Army. German radio listeners on the two fronts began to pick up signals from Rennenkampf to Samsonov in the new cipher, of which they could make nothing; then messages from Samsonov to Rennenkampf in the old peacetime army cipher. But Rennenkampf's operators had already followed orders to destroy their copies of that old cipher; they could no longer read it; and soon there were on the air requests from either Russian commander to the other to send his messages in clear, as the cipher was illegible.

The date had now reached August 20, 1914; that night there came through the air in radio clear a message from Rennenkampf to Samsonov saying the former was halting his advance for three days to let his supply trains catch up with the troops. Hindenburg and Ludendorff had just taken over command of the Germans on the front, with armies superior to either of the Russians alone, desperately inferior to the two together. At first they could not believe the Russians were publicly announcing their plans in this fashion. But as with von Kluck's move to the Marne, airplane and cavalry reconnaissance confirmed the fact of Rennenkampf's halt. Hindenburg flung out a screen of horsemen to keep the Rennenkampf army under observation, switched his divisions toward Poland along the excellent Germany military railroads, and on August 26th was in position against Samsonov, gripping him tight in front, with strong forces circling both his flanks. The three days following were known as the Battle of Tannenburg, not a battle but a massacre, for Samsonov's army was wiped out with a hundred thousand men dead or prisoners, and in the wild night of rain and defeat on the third day, the Russian commander shot himself. Three weeks later Rennenkampf also was crushed and Russia slid down the long gradient into ruin and revolution.

Yet while Russian soldiers were dying or marching off to prisons, Russian sailors were winning one of the most spectacular victories of the code-war behind the war. Germany began the conflict as a blue-water nation, keeping her ships at sea and clashing with the British along the line of the blockade, and in the Baltic, where they had the upper hand, raiding along the Russian coast. It was on such a raid that their light cruiser *Magdeburg* ran hard aground during a fog.

When the mists cleared the Russian fleet was bearing down. The *Magdeburg*'s case was evidently hopeless and her captain sent an officer down for the secret naval codebooks, bound in lead. They were to be taken in a boat as far from the ship as possible and thrown in deep water. The approaching Russians began to shoot; there was some confusion on the wrecked cruiser, and as the officer with the codebooks in his arms stood by the rail the heave of a swell pitched him into the water. An hour later the Russians had taken possession of the ship. One of their officers, in the old gentlemanly tradition of sea warfare, ordered the bodies round the ship taken up for decent burial. Seldom has an act of humanity been better rewarded; one of the first things the dredge drew up was the body of an officer with the lead bindings of codebooks in his arms.

The Russian captain rightly reasoned that where the bindings were found the stuffing could not be far away; he sent down a diver and within another hour had the German naval codebooks complete, somewhat damaged by seawater, but perfectly readable. England, as the head of the Allied naval effort, was notified at once, and a fast destroyer carried the books to London by way of the White Sea.

At this time the British Admiralty had already set up its famous decoding department—"Room 40"—under charge of Admiral Sir Reginald Hall, perhaps the best and most famous of all World War experts in secret service, cipher and espionage. Room 40 had been fumbling with German naval codes already; had made some slight progress, but not enough to be of importance when the godsend of the *Magdeburg's* books appeared. Not only did they furnish the code then in use, but also the key to the whole system on which the German naval codes were built, for Germany was using not one code but several.

They were all dictionary codes, consisting of a series of parallel columns, arranged somewhat in the following order, the left-hand column a list of words in dictionary order, the right-hand columns lists of code-signs:

	A	B	&C
Kreuzen	JACAB	LURLU	
Kreuzer	MUNTA	ACHEL	
Kriechen	NITZI	BELEB	
Krieg	ONIRD	ZURIT	

The code-words were in disordered arrangements and the several columns of them were obviously for the purpose of enabling codes to be changed from time to time. But the experts of Room 40 noticed that the B column opposite the words beginning with K in the clear (for instance) was the same as the A column opposite words beginning with M of the clear and the C column opposite words beginning with W of the clear. In other words, although a code group might signify different words on different days or even different hours, the same sequence of code-signs always stood for an alphabetical sequence of words.

This, in turn, meant that if a single code-sign could be identified with a clear word, after keys had been changed, all the code-signs in that column could be identified by merely setting down opposite the other signs in the column Germans words in alphabetical order. This was the decoding procedure Room 40 adopted; though the Germans changed keys fast and furiously, their radio messages were seldom a mystery for the two years following—or from the capture of the *Magdeburg* till after the Battle of Jutland—when the system was entirely recast.

This was to have the most important effects on the German naval effort, and through it on the whole course of the war. Twice in the early days the Germans tried slipping flotillas of destroyers down along the coast of Holland in an effort to raid British troop convoys across the Channel. Each time Room 40 read their radio signals and knew of the project. The first time fog and a storm forced the raiders back to harbor; the second time a fast and powerful British light cruiser waited across their path and sank four of the German ships before they could get away.

Twice, German battle-cruiser formations tried lightning raids across the North Sea against the English coast; each time England knew they were coming before they left harbor. On the first occasion missed orders and the Germans' own speed saved them from mishap, but on the second the British battle cruisers came swooping onto them from the morning mists at Dogger Bank. One German ship was sunk; two more staggered into port with flames leaping above their funnels, not to stir again till the last day of May in 1916, when they tried a trap for the British battle cruisers and were themselves trapped into the general fleet action off Jutland because Room 40 had again read their code signals.

The tragedy of that battle from the British point of view

was that Room 40 knew perfectly well where the German fleet was during the night of the fight, when Sir John Jellicoe was hunting for it. They tried to inform him but there was so much radio traffic in the air the message never got through; and the destroyers who did find the German battleships could do nothing. For the Germans, not bad at codework themselves, had noted during the long twilight the recognition signals flashed by one British ship to another for identification in the dark. When night came they flashed these same signals, and in the time thus gained blew the British destroyers out of the water, before they could warn their main fleet or fire torpedoes.

The event of Jutland seems to have brought Germany for the first time to the realization that her opponents must have solved her whole naval code system, but despite this slowness the Germans were by no means incompetent adversaries in the war of secret communications. By the middle of 1915 they had completely broken down both the British Playfairs and the ciphers then being used by the French, the German forces in the Black Sea worked a prodigious military joke on the Russians as a sequel to their success in solving Russian naval ciphers. The German ships *Göben* and *Breslau,* nominally under Turkish colors, were then based on Constantinople, and particularly anxious to accomplish something, though outnumbered by the Russian fleet. They waited till the latter put to sea, sneaked the speedy light cruiser *Breslau* in between the Russians and their base, and in Russian naval code, as though coming from home, wirelessed the Russian admiral orders to hurry his fleet to Trebizond, far at the eastern end of the Black Sea. When the puzzled Russian armada returned from this wildgoose chase they discovered the two German ships had raided their shore establishments and quite broken up their coastwise merchant shipping.

German also was one of the most brilliant cipher coups of the war. For months the great radio station at Nauen followed its regular evening broadcast of the daily communiqué with a series of signals emitted so rapidly they could hardly be considered separate sounds and resembled static more than anything else. The Allied code-rooms studied these signals for a long while, and came to believe they must represent some method of testing the apparatus, for this "lightning gibberish" came too fast and too incoherent to give any starting point toward solutions.

Accident, as not infrequently happens, furnished the clue. It was on a small British monitor, floating under the hot sun of an eastern Mediterranean harbor. The wardroom officers were trying to keep cool with the aid of long drinks and short musical selections played on a portable phonograph. Finally the officer in charge of the concert remarked:

"That's all except a record of some of Nauen's lightning gibberish."

"Put it on," said someone else. "Anything is better than nothing."

He put it on but forgot to rewind the phonograph, and everybody was too hot and tired to get up and wind it for him. As the instrument slowed toward the stopping point the record slowed with it; and as the record slowed, the high-pitched screech of the lightning gibberish turned into a perfectly rational series of radio code-groups. A code officer was among those present; he tried not only the single record but others of the lightning gibberish in dead slow time—and discovered that here was a series of messages from Germany's high command to General von Lettow-Vorbeck, commanding in German East Africa. They were in the prewar German Army cipher, which the Allies had long ago cracked. But it had been, of course, impossible to get the new ciphers through to him, and the Germans had adopted the ingenious trick of concealing the messages under speed. They were first recorded by means of a buzzer and the record played over the air at five or six times the normal velocity.

Yet it was a German wireless code that helped greatly in

bringing American indignation to the boiling point at which a declaration of war was asked. At Brussels a big radio station had been established for the dissemination of messages to German diplomats throughout the world. One of the operators at this station was an extremely talented young Austrian technician named Alexander Szek. The Germans had checked his background before placing him in so important a post, but they had not checked it carefully enough to discover that his mother was English and his personal sympathies bitterly anti-German.

In some manner the British Intelligence Service lighted on these important facts, and managed to get an emissary through the lines to Szek, who agreed to steal the German diplomatic code. It was a slow, painful, and dangerous job; Szek could only copy down from the big codebook a few words a day, seizing moments when he was alone, and hiding the slips with the results about his person till he could get home and pass them on to the English spy. The task took weeks and months, and when it had been completed Szek was informed he would have to stay at the Brussels station to prevent any suspicion reaching the Germans that their most secret diplomatic messages were being read in Room 40.

Of course, there came a time when the cat had to be let from the bag. It was the occasion of the famous Zimmermann message, early in 1917, when the German Ambassador to Mexico was instructed to work up an alliance with Japan to attack the United States with the aid of Mexico, and Mexico was offered three American states as her price. The news would do so much more damage to Germany if made public than if kept secret that Admiral Hall called in the reporters and gave them the text of the message.

At the end of the interview, "Wasn't it clever of the Americans," he asked, "to do just what we have been trying to do ever since the war started? They succeeded in stealing the original text of a German diplomatic telegram."

The press, British, French, and American, was taken in

by this piece of fake ingenuousness, but not the Germans. They began an investigation at the Brussels station and it became time for Alexander Szek to vanish. He met his friend the British agent, who got him out of Belgium and arranged passage to England and safety, but he never arrived in the British Isles. French sources say the British Intelligence Service themselves pushed him over the side of the boat during the trip to keep the Germans from finding out for certain what had happened. The only English writer who has touched the subject says German secret-service detectives followed the young man and caught up with him during the trip.

By the beginning of the 1917 campaigns it was evident on all fronts that even field ciphers could only be protected by changing not merely the keys, but the ciphers themselves, every few days. New German ciphers collapsed in the Allied Black Chambers under a few hours of analysis. The process was greatly helped by the Teutonic habit of wirelessing fixed test messages in each new cipher as it was issued. These test messages were usually proverbs, "A bird in the hand is worth two in the bush" (in its German version) being a great favorite. With a known text thus furnishing a whole series of probable words, Allied experts seldom had to do more than wait till they had their bird in hand with regard to any new cipher.

Transmitters' errors also played a part in breaking down German cipher messages. The Allies had warning of the great German drive of March 21, 1918, through a German cipher operator who used the wrong cipher, and the July Champagne drive which was turned into such a bloody defeat by the "Gouraud defense" is said to have been betrayed in its entirety through a ciphered wireless message. A new cipher had just been issued to all units along the German front, with the object of holding the orders for that drive secret. "New cipher not yet received" replied one of the German radio men in clear. "Please repeat message in old cipher." The message was repeated; the Allies had already broken the old cipher, and hence had parallel texts which completely destroyed the new.

Data with regard to the German methods of decipherment is rare, but it seems they made some use of the ciphering machines, occasionally in encipherments, more usually as calculating machines for operating decipherments. A number of these machines have appeared since the war; they are mostly alike in having a typewriter keyboard, with the keys connected through a series of cogs and cams to a set of adjusting screws or some device that fulfills the same purpose. When a message is typed on one of these machines, as the operator would type it on an ordinary typewriter, the cogs and cams operate automatically, imprinting on a tape a message in cipher. The recipient of such a message sets the variables on his own machine to the same points as the sender and types the message as received; the result recorded on his tape is the clear.

Theoretically these machines should produce a perfect cipher, as a given bigram of the clear, *TH* for example, will not appear enciphered by the same bigram more than once in four or five hundred appearances. Practically the machines are of very little use, particularly with an army. They are heavy and bulky, more difficult to transport than a dictionary code, get out of order readily, require a good supply of electric current, which is not always available in war. Finally, they are peculiarly subject to cipherers' errors; one touch on the wrong letter and the resulting message is gibberish. But there are variants on the same machines very useful for deciphering purposes in some classes of ciphers, particularly the complex disc ciphers, by automatically calculating numerical relations among the letters of a given cryptogram and sorting out resemblances. They can be defeated only by something that is not systematic at all—a full code—or something that is systematic only in a way of which a machine cannot take account—substitution combined with partial transposition.

Partial codes, in fact, were the universal development on

all the fighting fronts in the last two years of the war for communications even among minor units. The development of listening posts, wire-tapping devices and the induction coils that suck a telephone message into the enemy's lines made even ordinary conversation dangerous during the trench warfare period. "The greatest trouble experienced thus far on our front," says a general order sent to all German units in 1918, "has been due to intercepted telephone messages."

When the United States entered the war, our government thought it had the answer to this. A number of Choctaw Indians were sent into the trenches to 'phone messages to one another in their own tongue, with the idea that the Germans would have to go a long distance before finding Choctaw interpreters. The idea was a success as far as concealing the context of messages from the Germans, but it was too much of a success; the Indians were unable to understand one another over the telephone, and their language held no equivalents for such un-Indian devices as "barrage," "machine gun" and "zero hour."

Thus 1917 and 1918 saw the return of the old jargon-codes of the eighteenth century for all types of messages. Only a few words, and these the more important ones that would identify organizations and troop movements were included in these jargon-codes, which were short enough to be memorized or to be written on a single sheet of paper. A typical message by 'phone to a front-line battalion might be:

"Old Dreadnaught to Red Bonehead. You are receiving six jars of marmalade. In the pantry by forty-two o'clock." —Signifying that the divisional commander was sending three companies (subtract 3 from the 6 of the code) to support a front-line battalion, which was to start toward its objective at 6 A.M. (divide the code figure given by 7).

After the Germans changed their naval code, as the aftermath of Jutland Battle, there was a considerable space of time during which Room 40 of the British Admiralty had a

good deal of difficulty. Then unrestricted submarine warfare began, and war against the submarines on a basis as
unrestricted. One of the undersea boats—it has never been
told which or when—was sunk in shallow water near the
British coast. She lay so near the surface that England sent
down divers to learn what they could of the latest devices
aboard, and one of these divers found on the wrecked submarine, in a watertight compartment near the conning
tower, the latest codebook of the submarine service.

Submarine commanders, whether from the loneliness of
their business or from a natural desire to boast of their exploits, were notoriously chatty men. They usually came to
the surface at night and talked by the hour with one another
and home in radio code. Now that the British had the new
codes, the key of these communications was unlocked; but
it soon became evident to the Germans that their enemies
had the secret and they changed codes. The British had
found the answer to that: every time a submarine was sunk
in waters at all possible for diving operations men were sent
down. Sure enough, the systematic Teutons kept their codebooks in the same place aboard every submarine, and
though the work of extracting them was hard and dangerous, British divers got enough of these codebooks to
keep them well abreast of the latest developments.

Two things were lacking. One was a list of the submarines' call letters, the identifying signatures with which
every message opened. Sometimes these letters could be
identified from other sources—remarks in the submarine
radio conversations themselves, ships that had been attacked, but escaped with notes as to the numbers painted
on the conning towers of the tin fish that had tried to sink
them. Thus *LOL* would be identified as *UB-46*. But a radio
station might pick up *LOL* a week later, and discover that
it was not *UB-46* at all, but *U-108;* and changes like this
seemed to take place at irregular intervals without rhyme
or reason.

The other point lacking was with regard to the positions

of the submarines. One of the undersea boats would come to the surface and chatter for a time, then dive before British directional wireless could do more than approximately locate the position from which she was talking. In her messages there would always be certain letter groups which were presumably code for her position. But these position code-signs were constructed on an arbitrary system, and no key to them was found in any of the sunken boats. Apparently it was something that submarine commanders were required to memorize, or which they carried in some other place than the ordinary haunt of the codebooks.

In October, 1917, came the last of the great Zeppelin raids on London. Returning from the raid the big gas-bags ran into an unexpected head storm over the English Channel. Four of them used up all their fuel bucking the gale and, toward dawn of the next day, drifted helplessly south across France with their motors dead. Two of these four kept close together, L-49 and L-51. The latter bumped and scratched through the upper branches of a swampy wood, tore loose one of her power cars and, relieved of this weight, rose again and drifted off to disappear forever in the Mediterranean. L-49 settled gently and, after scraping the trees in her turn, nestled in a field near Chaumont, where she was captured by an astonished and ancient *garde champêtre*.

Chaumont was American Army headquarters, and within half an hour of the Zeppelin's descent, the place was swarming with staff officers. One of these officers was Colonel Richard Williams of the United States Army Intelligence section, to whom it occurred that the men of the wrecked airship must have been considerably embarrassed by the presence of their codebooks. They could hardly have sunk them in the manner of a failing ship; the last water they had crossed was the English Channel. Neither could the books have been burned aboard that hydrogen-filled bag, and when a search failed to reveal any traces of codebooks, orders or other official papers on the prisoners, Williams deduced they must have been torn up and thrown overboard in fragments.

Carrying his reasoning one step farther, he believed that this job must have been carried out as L-49 skimmed the treetops on the way to her last landing, and gathering a detail of men, he set out on the back track the balloon had left through the trees. A quarter of a mile back he began to find scraps of paper and then a perfect snowfall. Before night he and his detail had gathered no less than twenty-two gunnysacks full of pieces.

It was too much. When Lieutenant Samuel Hubbard of the staff entered the barnlike map-room at headquarters about midnight that night to see what was going on, he found Williams and half a dozen privates working gigantic jigsaw puzzles all over the place and not having much luck with them. There were so many different papers represented, with parts of all missing, that it seemed impossible to match them up coherently. Hubbard was an amateur yachtsman, who before the war had sailed a small boat through the Danish Islands. The faintly blue color of a fragment about the size of the palm of his hand attracted his attention. When he picked it up he recognized a line that jagged across the piece as the outline of a bay where he had put in with his boat. It was, then, a piece of a chart; yet different from any chart he had ever seen, for it was crossed by fine ruled lines, at the intersection of which were sets of letters.

This seemed to him important. He persuaded Colonel Williams to have the men dig out more fragments of the chart, readily recognizable by their blue color, and easy to piece together because of its map character. It was a big chart, covering all German waters, the whole North Sea and all the sections of ocean that washed the British Isles and northern France. It was, in fact, the thing the Allies had been hunting for for two years—a code-chart, the complete key to those mysterious code-signs giving the positions of the submarines. Nor was this all; as Hubbard, Williams, and the detail labored at piecing together the big chart, one of the men produced from his pocket a little book and inquired whether it had anything to do with the chart. He had found it among the pieces of paper and "saved it as a sort of souvenir." It contained a photograph of every surface ship and submarine in the Imperial Germany Navy, with a list of the call letters for each and a key to the changes in the call letters.

This was how it came about that November, 1917, was the black month of the submarines, with six sent to the bottom and their own sinkings falling to a low from which they never recovered.